christmas source

A comprehensive seasonal collection

We hope you enjoy *Christmas Source*. Further copies are available
from your local Kevin Mayhew stockist.

In case of difficulty, or to request a catalogue,
please contact the publisher direct by writing to:

The Sales Department
KEVIN MAYHEW LTD
Buxhall
Stowmarket
Suffolk IP14 3BW

Phone 01449 737978
Fax 01449 737834
E-mail info@kevinmayhewltd.com

First published in Great Britain in 2002 by Kevin Mayhew Ltd.

© Copyright 2002 Kevin Mayhew Ltd.

ISBN 1 84003 945 0
ISMN M 57024 109 5
Catalogue No: 1470130

1 2 3 4 5 6 7 8 9

Cover design by Angela Selfe

Printed and bound in Great Britain

Important Copyright Information

The Publishers wish to express their gratitude to the copyright owners who have granted permission to include their copyright material in this book. Full details are indicated on the respective pages.

The **words** of most of the songs in this publication are covered by a **Church Copyright Licence** which is available from Christian Copyright Licensing International. This allows local church reproduction on overhead projector acetates, in service bulletins, songsheets, audio/visual recording and other formats.

The **music** in this book is covered by the additional **Music Reproduction Licence** which is issued by CCLI in the territories of Europe and Australasia. You may photocopy the music and words of the songs in the book provided:

> You hold a current Music Reproduction Licence from CCLI.

> The copyright owner of the song you intend to photocopy is included in the Authorised Catalogue List which comes with your Music Reproduction Licence.

The Music Reproduction Licence is **not** currently available in the USA or Canada.

Full details of CCLI can be obtained from their Web site (www.ccli.com) or you can contact them direct at the following offices:

Christian Copyright Licensing (Europe) Ltd
PO Box 1339, Eastbourne, East Sussex, BN21 1AD, UK
Tel: +44 (0)1323 417711; Fax: +44 (0)1323 417722; E-mail: info@ccli.co.uk

CCL Asia-Pacific Pty Ltd (Australia and New Zealand)
PO Box 6644, Baulkham Hills Business Centre, NSW 2153, Australia
Tel: +61 (02) 9894-5386; Toll Free Phone: 1-800-635-474
Fax: +61 (02) 9894-5701; Toll Free Fax: 1-800-244-477
E-mail executive@ccli.co.au

Christian Copyright Licensing Inc
17201 NE Sacramento Street, Portland, Oregon 97230, USA
Tel: +1 (503) 257 2230; Toll Free Phone: 1 (800) 234 2446;
Fax: +1 (503) 257 2244; E-mail executive@ccli.com

Please note, all texts and music in this book are protected by copyright and if you do <u>not</u> possess a licence from CCLI they may <u>not</u> be reproduced in any way for sale or private use without the consent of the copyright owner.

Christmas Source is the definitive collection of carols, hymns and songs for the Christmas season.

Alongside well-loved traditional carols are seasonal worship songs, children's songs and even new arrangements of old tunes.

This unique blend of old and new will undoubtedly prove to be an invaluable resource to many.

1 A baby was born in Bethlehem

Words and Music: Ivor Golby

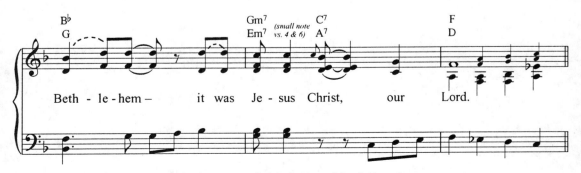

2. They laid him in a manger, *(x3)*
   where the oxen feed on hay.

3. Some shepherds heard the glad tidings, *(x3)*
   from an angel in the sky.

4. They left their flocks a-sleeping, *(x3)*
   and hurried to Bethlehem.

5. Three wise men came from far lands, *(x3)*
   they were guided by a star.

6. They laid their gifts before him, *(x3)*
   and worshipped on bended knee.

7. Then ev'rybody be happy, *(x3)*
   on the birthday of our Lord!

2 A great and mighty wonder

Words: St Germanus
trans. John Mason Neale

Music: German carol melody,
harmonies based on Michael Praetorius, alt.

ES IST EIN' ROS' ENTSPRUNGEN 76 76 676

1. A great and migh-ty won-der, a full and ho-ly cure!

The Vir-gin bears the in-fant with vir-gin - hon - our pure:

Chorus

Re - peat the hymn a - gain! 'To God on high be

glo - ry, and peace on earth shall reign.'

2. The Word becomes incarnate,
   and yet remains on high;
   and cherubim sing anthems
   to shepherds from the sky:

3. While thus they sing your monarch,
   those bright angelic bands,
   rejoice, ye vales and mountains,
   ye oceans, clap your hands:

4. Since all he comes to ransom
   by all be he adored,
   the infant born in Bethl'em,
   the Saviour and the Lord:

3 Ain't nothing like it

Words and Music: Graham Kendrick

To chorus

2. Ain't no - thing - prise.

Chorus 1

Seemed like an - gels

jumped right out of hea - ven, land - ed dan - cing down

here. My head is ring - ing with

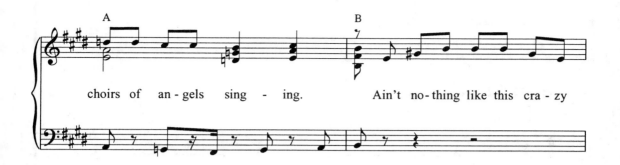

choirs of an-gels sing - ing. Ain't no-thing like this cra - zy

day.

2. Ain't nothing like it,
   this wild experience;
   could not believe my
   own ears and eyes.
   I thought I'd died and
   I'd gone to heaven.
   Ain't nothing like this big surprise.

3. Ain't nothing like it,
   the news they told us,
   for us a Saviour,
   a baby boy;
   born in a stable,
   the One we're looking for,
   he must be heaven's pride and joy.

Chorus 2   *So excited,*
what a birthday party,
Hallelujah O yeah!
So delighted,
we have been invited
to celebrate
his happy day.

RAP

Chorus 3   *Glory, hallelujah,*
heaven's peace and joy be to you.
Everything is alright now.
Let's sing it, and shout it,
tell the world about it.
Ain't nothing like
this happy feeling.

Ain't nothing like this crazy day.
Come on and join this happy day.

4 All hail King Jesus!

Words and Music: Dave Moody

5 All my heart this night rejoices

Words: Paul Gerhardt
trans. Catherine Winkworth

Melody and bass
by Johann Georg Ebeling

BONN 8 33 6 D

1. All my heart this night re - joi - ces, as I hear, far and near, sweet - est an - gel voi - ces: 'Christ is born!' their choirs are sing - ing, till the air ev - 'ry - where now with joy is ring - ing.

2. Hark, a voice from yonder manger,
   soft and sweet,
   doth entreat,
   'Flee from woe and danger;
   come, O come; from all doth grieve you
   you are freed,
   all you need
   I will surely give you.'

3. Come then, let us hasten yonder;
   here let all,
   great and small,
   kneel in awe and wonder;
   love him who with love is yearning;
   hail the star
   that from far
   bright with hope is burning!

4. Thee, O Lord, with heed I'll cherish,
   live to thee,
   and with thee
   dying, shall not perish;
   but shall dwell with thee for ever,
   far on high,
   in the joy
   that can alter never.

6 A long time ago

Words and Music: Susanna Levell
arr. Chris Mitchell

Note: This can be sung as a round:
at the end of verse 2, half the singers continue,
while the other half start verse 2 again and then continue

2. Some shepherds were watching
   over their sheep at night time. Ah.
   An angel of God
   brought news of the new-born Saviour. Ah.

3. Some wise men were trav'lling
   far from the east to see him. Ah.
   They followed a star
   that led them to Christ the Saviour. Ah.

4. A long time ago a baby
   was born in Bethlehem. Ah.
   The Light of the world,
   the Saviour of all, King Jesus. Ah.

7 Amazing grace! *(Amazing grace - I was homeless)*

Words: v.1 John Newton;
vs. 2, 3 Graham Kendrick

Music: American folk melody
adapted by Graham Kendrick

1. A - ma - zing grace! How sweet the sound that saved a wretch like me. I once was lost, but now am found; was blind, but now I see.

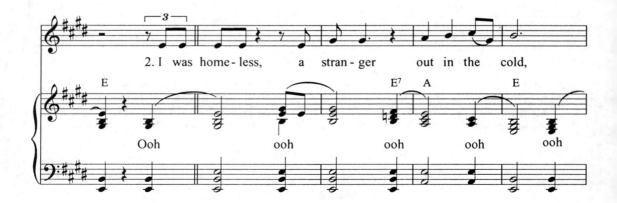

2. I was home - less, a stran - ger out in the cold,

Ooh ooh ooh ooh ooh

8 Angels from the realms of glory

Words: James Montgomery

Music: French or Flemish melody

IRIS 87 87 47

1. An-gels from the realms of glo-ry, wing your flight o'er all the earth;

ye, who sang cre - a -tion's sto - ry, now pro-claim Mes - si - ah's birth:

Chorus

Come ... and wor - ship,

Come ... and

Christ, the new-born King; come

Come

and wor - ship, wor - ship Christ the new - born King.

and

2. Shepherds in the field abiding,
   watching o'er your flocks by night,
   God with us is now residing,
   yonder shines the infant light:

3. Sages, leave your contemplations;
   brighter visions beam afar;
   seek the great desire of nations;
   ye have seen his natal star:

4. Saints, before the altar bending,
   watching long with hope and fear,
   suddenly the Lord, descending,
   in his temple shall appear:

9 Angels we have heard on high

Words: Traditional French carol

Music: Traditional French or Flemish melody
arr. Simon Anderson

IRIS 77 77 and Refrain

1. Angels we have heard on high, sweetly singing o'er the plains; and the mountains in reply, echoing their joyous strains. Glo - - ri - a

in ex - cel - sis De - o! Glo -
- - ri - a
in ex - cel - sis De - o!

2. Shepherds, why this jubilee?
   Why your joyous strains prolong?
   What the gladsome tidings be
   which inspire your heav'nly song?

3. Come to Bethlehem, and see
   him whose birth the angels sing.
   Come, adore on bended knee
   Christ the Lord, the new-born King.

4. See him in a manger laid,
   whom the choirs of angels praise.
   Mary, Joseph, lend your aid,
   while our hearts in love we raise.

10 Angel-voices ever singing

Words: Francis Pott alt.

Music: Edwin George Monk

ANGEL VOICES 85 85 843

1. An-gel-voi-ces e-ver sing-ing round thy throne of light,
an-gel-harps for e-ver ring-ing, rest not day nor night;
thou-sands on-ly live to bless thee, and con-fess thee Lord of might.

2. Thou who art beyond the farthest
mortal eye can see,
can it be that thou regardest
our poor hymnody?
Yes, we know that thou art near us
and wilt hear us constantly.

3. Yea, we know that thou rejoicest
o'er each work of thine;
thou didst ears and hands and voices
for thy praise design;
craftsman's art and music's measure
for thy pleasure all combine.

4. In thy house, great God, we offer
of thine own to thee;
and for thine acceptance proffer,
all unworthily,
hearts and minds and hands and voices
in our choicest psalmody.

5. Honour, glory, might and merit
thine shall ever be,
Father, Son and Holy Spirit,
blessèd Trinity.
Of the best that thou hast given
earth and heaven render thee.

11 A special star

Words: Laura and Heather Bradley

Music: Laura Bradley
arr. Chris Mitchell

Calypso

1. A spe-cial star is in the sky to

lead the way (to lead the way); a ti - ny sta - ble,

cold and lone - ly, where they can stay (where they can stay).

Chorus

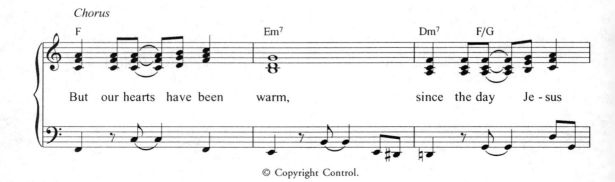

But our hearts have been warm, since the day Je - sus

Christ, was born, and that's the way it should stay, be-cause

he is the way, the truth and the life, (the truth and the life).

2. The shepherds left their flocks behind
   to see the babe (to see the babe);
   the angel told them to bring a gift so
   a lamb they gave (a lamb they gave).

3. The wise men came from lands afar,
   on camels they rode (on camels they rode);
   the gifts they offered were frankincense,
   myrrh and gold (myrrh and gold).

12 As with gladness men of old

Words: William Chatterton Dix

Music: adapted from Conrad Kocher
by William Henry Monk

DIX 77 77 77

2. As with joyful steps they sped,
   to that lowly manger-bed,
   there to bend the knee before
   him whom heav'n and earth adore,
   so may we with willing feet
   ever seek thy mercy-seat.

3. As their precious gifts they laid,
   at thy manger roughly made,
   so may we with holy joy,
   pure, and free from sin's alloy,
   all our costliest treasures bring,
   Christ, to thee our heav'nly King.

4. Holy Jesu, ev'ry day
   keep us in the narrow way;
   and, when earthly things are past,
   bring our ransomed souls at last
   where they need no star to guide,
   where no clouds thy glory hide.

5. In the heav'nly country bright
   need they no created light,
   thou its light, its joy, its crown,
   thou its sun which goes not down;
   there for ever may we sing
   alleluias to our King.

13 At this time of giving

(The giving song)

Words and Music: Graham Kendrick

2. May his tender love surround you
   at this Christmastime;
   may you see his smiling face
   that in the darkness shines.

3. But the many gifts he gives
   are all poured out from one;
   come, receive the greatest gift,
   the gift of God's own Son.

Last two choruses and verses:
   Lai, lai, lai . . .*etc.*

14 Away in a manger

Words: Unknown

Music: William James Kirkpatrick arr. Richard Lloyd

TUNE 1: CRADLE SONG 11 11 11 11

2. The cattle are lowing, the baby awakes,
   but little Lord Jesus no crying he makes.
   I love thee, Lord Jesus! Look down from the sky,
   and stay by my side until morning is nigh.

3. Be near me, Lord Jesus; I ask thee to stay
   close by me for ever, and love me, I pray.
   Bless all the dear children in thy tender care,
   and fit us for heaven, to live with thee there.

Words: Unknown
Music: William James Kirkpatrick
Alternative verses 2 & 3 by Michael Forster

James R. Murray

TUNE 2: MUELLER 11 11 11 11

1. A - way in a man - ger, no crib for a bed, the lit - tle Lord

Je - sus laid down his sweet head. The stars in the bright sky looked

down where he lay, the lit - tle Lord Je - sus a - sleep on the hay.

2. The cattle are lowing, the baby awakes,
   but little Lord Jesus no crying he makes.
   I love thee, Lord Jesus! Look down from the sky,
   and stay by my side until morning is nigh.

3. Be near me, Lord Jesus; I ask thee to stay
   close by me for ever, and love me, I pray.
   Bless all the dear children in thy tender care,
   and fit us for heaven, to live with thee there.

Alternative text for verses 2 and 3:

2. The cattle are lowing, they also adore
   the little Lord Jesus who lies in the straw.
   I love you, Lord Jesus, I know you are near
   to love and protect me till morning is here.

3. Be near me, Lord Jesus; I ask you to stay
   close by me for ever, and love me, I pray.
   Bless all the dear children in your tender care,
   prepare us for heaven, to live with you there.

15 Behold, the great Creator makes

Words: Thomas Pestel

Music: Albert Lister Peace

GREEN HILL CM

1. Behold, the great Cre - a - tor makes him - self a house of clay; a robe of hu - man form he takes for e - ver from this day.

2. Hear this! the wise eternal Word
   as Mary's infant cries;
   a servant is our mighty Lord,
   and God in cradle lies.

3. This wonder all the world amazed
   and shook the starry frame;
   the hosts of heaven stood and gazed,
   then blessed the Saviour's name.

4. Glad shepherds run to view this sight,
   a choir of angels sings;
   and eastern magi with delight
   adore this King of kings.

5. Join then, all hearts that are not stone,
   and all our voices prove
   to celebrate the holy One,
   the God of peace and love.

16 Born in the night, Mary's child

Words and Music: Geoffrey Ainger

MARY'S CHILD 76 76

1. Born in the night, Ma-ry's child, a long way from your home;

com - ing in need, Ma-ry's child, born in a bor-rowed room.

2. Clear shining light,
   Mary's child,
   your face lights up our way;
   light of the world,
   Mary's child,
   dawn on our darkened day.

3. Truth of our life,
   Mary's child,
   you tell us God is good;
   prove it is true,
   Mary's child,
   go to your cross of wood.

4. Hope of the world,
   Mary's child,
   you're coming soon to reign;
   King of the earth,
   Mary's child,
   walk in our streets again.

17 Break forth, O beauteous heavenly light

Words: v.1 Johann Rist,
trans. John Troutbeck;
v.2 A.T. Russell

Music: Melody by Johann Schop,
harm. Johann Sebastian Bach

ERMUNTRE DICH MEIN SCHWACHER Irregular

1. Break forth, O beau- teous heav'n- ly light, and ush- er in the morn- ing; O shep- herds, shrink not with af- fright, but hear the an- gel's warn- ing. This child, now weak in in- fan- cy, our con- fi- dence and

joy shall be, the pow'r of Sa - tan break - ing, our peace e - ter - nal mak - ing.

2. Break forth, O beauteous heav'nly light,
   to herald our salvation;
   he stoops to earth – the God of might,
   our hope and expectation.
   He comes in human flesh to dwell,
   our God with us, Immanuel,
   the night of darkness ending,
   our fallen race befriending.

18 Brightest and best

Words: Reginald Heber

Music: Joseph Francis Thrupp

EPIPHANY 11 10 11 10

2. Cold on his cradle the dew-drops are shining;
   low lies his head with the beasts of the stall:
   angels adore him, in slumber reclining,
   maker and monarch, and Saviour of all.

3. Say, shall we yield him, in costly devotion,
   odours of Edom, and off'rings divine;
   gems of the mountain, and pearls of the ocean,
   myrrh from the forest, or gold from the mine?

4. Vainly we offer each ample oblation;
   vainly with gifts would his favour secure;
   richer by far is the heart's adoration;
   dearer to God are the prayers of the poor.

5. Brightest and best of the suns of the morning,
   dawn on our darkness and lend us thine aid;
   star of the east, the horizon adorning,
   guide where our infant Redeemer is laid.

19 Call his name *(Mary woke with a start one night)*

Words and Music: Phil Overton
arr. Chris Mitchell

20 Can you believe it

Words and Music: Graham Kendrick

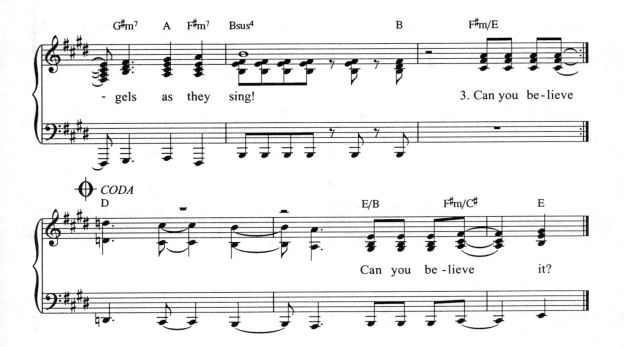

Can you believe it?

3. Can you believe it?
His name shall be called Wonderful.
Can you believe it?
Counsellor, Mighty God.
Can you believe it?
Everlasting Father.
Can you believe it?
He is the Prince of Peace.

4. Can you believe it?
This is good news, good news.
Can you believe it?
Don't be afraid!
Can you believe it?
The sun of Righteousness has dawned.
Can you believe it?
Joy to the world!
Can you believe it?
He came to seek, to save the lost.
Can you believe it?
Peace on earth!
Can you believe it? (believe it),
Oh, can you believe it?

21 Can you see what we have made *(Song for Christingle)*

Words and Music: Graham Kendrick

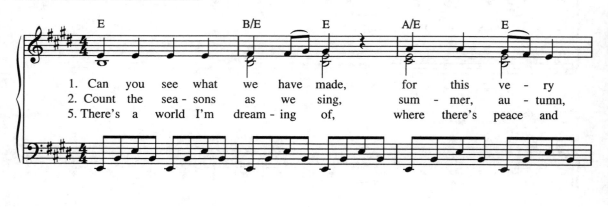

1. Can you see what we have made, for this ve – ry
2. Count the sea – sons as we sing, sum – mer, au – tumn,
5. There's a world I'm dream – ing of, where there's peace and

spe – cial day? An o – range for our pla – net home
win – ter, spring. Sing to God who sends the rain,
joy and love. Light of Je – sus ev – 'ry – where,

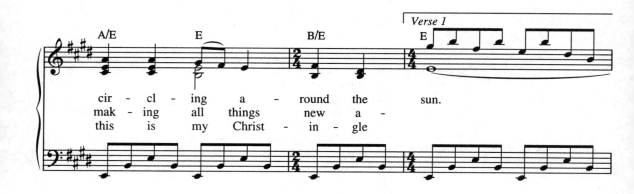

Verse 1

cir – cl – ing a – round the sun.
mak – ing all things new a –
this is my Christ – in – gle

Verses 2 and 5

2. gain.
5. prayer.

22 Carols sing

Words: Paul E. Puckett and Martha Puckett

Music: Martha Puckett

BETHLEHEM SONG Irregular

1. Carols sing to the King, Jesus Christ our Saviour;

born this day, angels say, in a lowly manger;

he came down to the earth bringing us new birth.

Carols sing to the King, Jesus Christ our Saviour.

2. Tidings bring! to the King,
   shepherds did adore him;
   from afar, by the star,
   wise men sought and found him.
   Praise his name throughout the earth,
   tell the joyful news.
   Victor now, o'er the grave,
   Jesus Christ was born to save.

3. Carols sing to the King,
   Jesus Christ our Saviour;
   Wonderful Counsellor,
   mighty God, Redeemer,
   Son of God, Son of man –
   all in all I see.
   Carols raise, his name praise,
   he shall reign eternally.

23 C for the Christ Child
(Sing a song about Christmas)

Words and Music: Dave Cooke

24 Child in the manger

Words: Mary MacDonald
trans. Lachlan MacBean

Music: Traditional Gaelic melody
arr. Colin Hand

BUNESSAN 55 53 D

1. Child in the man - ger, in - fant of Ma - ry; out - cast and stran - ger, Lord of all; child who in - he - rits all our trans - gres - sions, all our de - me - rits on him fall.

2. Once the most holy child of salvation
gently and lowly lived below;
now as our glorious mighty Redeemer,
see him victorious o'er each foe.

3. Prophets foretold him, infant of wonder;
angels behold him on his throne;
worthy our Saviour of all their praises;
happy for ever are his own.

25 Child of the stable's secret birth

Words: Timothy Dudley-Smith

Music: Valerie Ruddle

FOYE 89 99 98

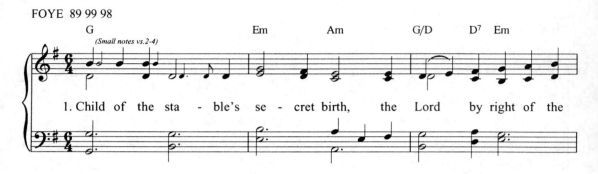

1. Child of the sta - ble's se - cret birth, the Lord by right of the

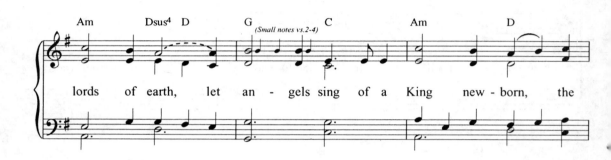

lords of earth, let an - gels sing of a King new - born, the

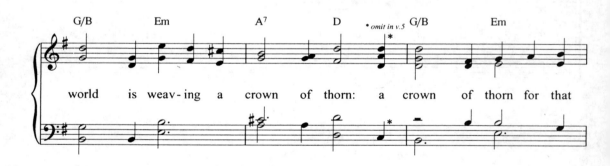

world is weav - ing a crown of thorn: a crown of thorn for that

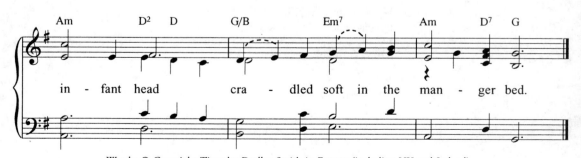

in - fant head cra - dled soft in the man - ger bed.

2. Eyes that shine in the lantern's ray;
   a face so small in its nest of hay,
   face of a child who is born to scan
   the world he made through the eyes of man:
   and from that face in the final day
   earth and heaven shall flee away.

3. Voice that rang through the courts on high
   contracted now to a wordless cry,
   a voice to master the wind and wave, M
   the human heart and the hungry grave:
   the voice of God through the cedar trees
   rolling forth as the sound of seas.

4. Infant hands in a mother's hand,
   for none but Mary may understand
   whose are the hands and the fingers curled W
   but his who fashioned and made our world;
   and through these hands in the hour of death
   nails shall strike to the wood beneath.

5. Child of the stable's secret birth,
   the Father's gift to a wayward earth,
   to drain the cup in a few short years
   of all our sorrows, our sins and tears;
   ours the prize for the road he trod:
   risen with Christ; at peace with God.

26 Christians, awake!

Words: John Byrom, alt.

Music: John Wainwright

YORKSHIRE (STOCKPORT) 10 10 10 10 10 10

1. Christ - ians, a - wake! Sa - lute the hap - py morn,

where - on the Sa - viour of the world was born;

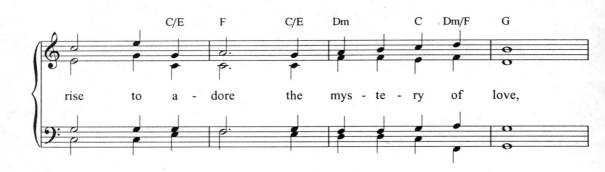

rise to a - dore the mys - te - ry of love,

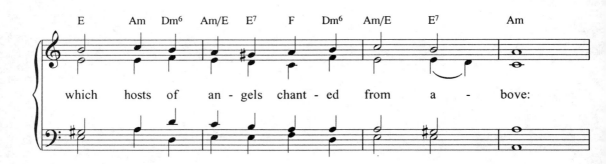

which hosts of an - gels chant - ed from a - bove:

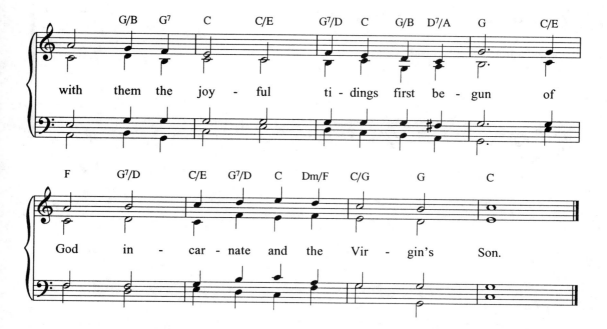

with them the joy - ful ti - dings first be - gun of

God in - car - nate and the Vir - gin's Son.

2. Then to the watchful shepherds it was told,
   who heard th'angelic herald's voice, 'Behold,
   I bring good tidings of a Saviour's birth
   to you and all the nations on the earth:
   this day hath God fulfilled his promised word,
   this day is born a Saviour, Christ the Lord.'

3. He spake; and straightway the celestial choir
   in hymns of joy, unknown before, conspire;
   the praises of redeeming love they sang,
   and heav'n's whole orb with alleluias rang:
   God's highest glory was their anthem still,
   peace on the earth, in ev'ry heart good will.

4. To Bethl'em straight th'enlightened shepherds ran,
   to see, unfolding, God's eternal plan,
   and found, with Joseph and the blessèd maid,
   her Son, the Saviour, in a manger laid:
   then to their flocks, still praising God, return,
   and their glad hearts with holy rapture burn.

5. O may we keep and ponder in our mind
   God's wondrous love in saving lost mankind;
   trace we the babe, who hath retrieved our loss,
   from his poor manger to his bitter cross;
   tread in his steps, assisted by his grace,
   till our first heav'nly state again takes place.

6. Then may we hope, th'angelic hosts among,
   to sing, redeemed, a glad triumphal song:
   he that was born upon this joyful day
   around us all his glory shall display;
   saved by his love, incessant we shall sing
   eternal praise to heav'n's almighty King.

27 Christmas bells that bring *(Heaven's gift of love)*

Words and Music: James Wright
arr. Chris Mitchell

1. Christ-mas bells that bring glad tid-ings, ca-rols full of joy and cheer.

Fai-ry lights that shine and glis-ten, how I love this time of year.

But with-in my heart I che-rish, more than all my eyes can see,

one small child laid in a man-ger, hea-ven's gift of love to me.

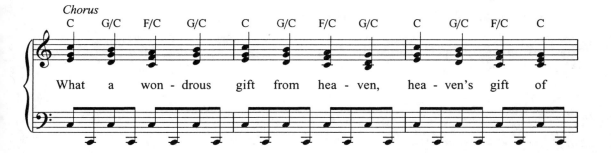

What a won-drous gift from hea-ven, hea-ven's gift of

love to me. One small ba-by in a man-ger,

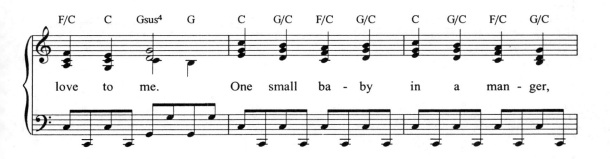

hea-ven's gift of love to me.

2. Christmas carols and decorations,
   choc'lates on the Christmas tree.
   Giving gifts to one another,
   meeting friends and family.
   But within my heart I cherish,
   more than all my eyes can see,
   one small child laid in a manger,
   heaven's gift of love to me.

28 Christmas is a time to love

Words and Music: Ernie and Debbie Rettino
arr. Chris Mitchell

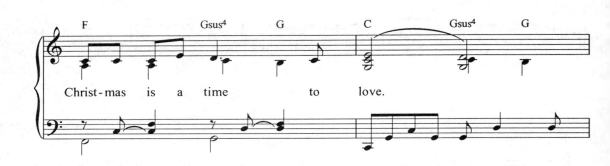

of – ten start to wor – ry,   and   peo – ple get up – set   if

things don't all go right on Christ – mas Day.

What we should re – mem – ber in all the push and shove,   is

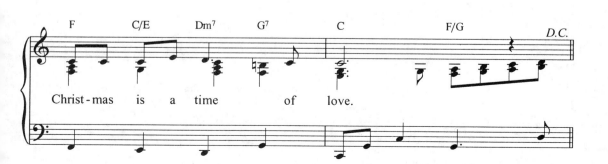

Christ – mas is a time of love.

29 Christmas isn't Christmas

Words and Music: Jimmy and Carol Owens
arr. Chris Mitchell

30 Christmas, it's Christmas

Words and Music: Capt. Alan Price, CA.

31 Christmas without Jesus

Words and Music: Capt. Alan J. Price CA
arr. Chris Mitchell

out the Christ of Christ-mas, it would not be the same. He's the
he's the Christ of Christ-mas, he's the Lord that we pro-claim. He's the

rea - son for the sea - son, we re - mem - ber that he came; with -
rea - son for the sea - son, we re - mem - ber Je - sus came; and

out the Christ of Christ-mas, it would not be the same.
he's the Christ of Christ-mas, he's the Lord that we pro - claim.

2. Christmas without Jesus is what many people have,
   they celebrate, but don't remember why.
   They've forgotten God's Son, Jesus,
   who came that holy night,
   to show how much God loves us,
   so much that he would die.

3. Christmas without Jesus leaves an emptiness inside,
   an emptiness that nothing else can fill,
   so come on ev'rybody,
   let's sing the angels' song,
   God's gift of love in Jesus,
   of peace and of goodwill.

32 Come and join the celebration

Words and Music: Valerie Collison

CELEBRATIONS 11 14 and Refrain

Come and join the ce-le-bra-tion, it's a ve-ry spe-cial day;

come and share our ju-bi-la-tion, there's a new King born to-day!

1. See the shep-herds hur-ry down to Beth-le-hem;

gaze in won-der at the Son of God who lay be-fore them.

Chorus

Come and join the ce-le-bra-tion, it's a ve-ry spe-cial day;

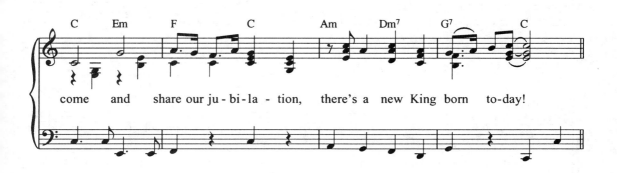

come and share our ju-bi-la-tion, there's a new King born to-day!

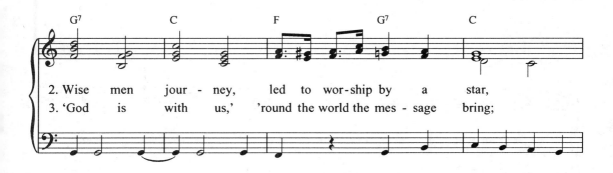

2. Wise men jour-ney, led to wor-ship by a star,
3. 'God is with us,' 'round the world the mes-sage bring;

2nd time D.C. al Fine

kneel in hom-age, bring-ing pre-cious gifts from lands a-far, so
he is with us, 'Wel-come!' all the bells on earth are peal-ing.

33 Come and praise the Lord our King

Words: Traditional, adapted by
Geoffrey Marshall-Taylor

Music: Traditional
arr. Chris Mitchell

Brightly

Chorus D ... G D

Come and praise the Lord our King, hal-le-lu - jah, come and

Bm⁷ Em⁷ G/A A⁷ D D

Last time / To continue

praise the Lord our King, hal-le-lu - jah. jah. 1. Christ was

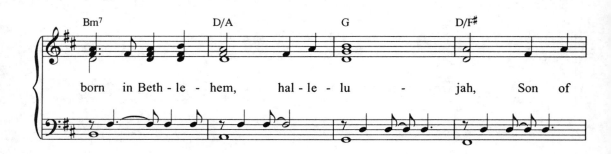

Bm⁷ D/A G D/F♯

born in Beth-le-hem, hal-le-lu - jah, Son of

F♯m Em G/A A⁷ D Chorus D.S.

God and Son of Man, hal-le-lu - jah. Come and

2. From him love and wisdom came,
   hallelujah,
   all his life was free from blame,
   hallelujah.

3. Jesus died at Calvary,
   hallelujah,
   rose again triumphantly,
   hallelujah.

4. He will cleanse us from our sin,
   hallelujah,
   if we live by faith in him,
   hallelujah.

5. He will be with us today,
   hallelujah,
   and for ever with us stay,
   hallelujah.

6. We will live with him one day,
   hallelujah,
   and for ever with him stay,
   hallelujah.

34 Come, come, come to the manger

Words: Unknown, alt.

Music: Traditional melody
adapted by S.P. Waddington

COME TO THE MANGER Irregular and Refrain

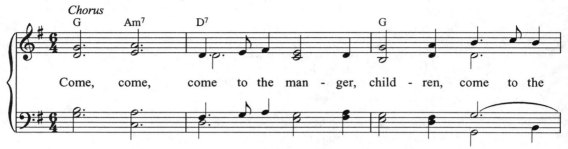

Come, come, come to the man - ger, child - ren, come to the

child - ren's King; sing, sing, cho - rus of an - gels,

star of morn - ing o'er Beth - le - hem sing. 1. He lies 'mid the beasts of the

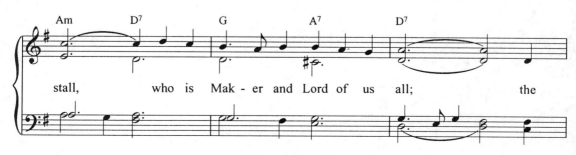

stall, who is Mak - er and Lord of us all; the

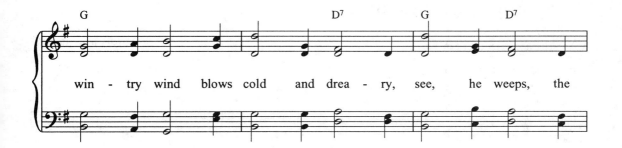

win - try wind blows cold and drea - ry, see, he weeps, the

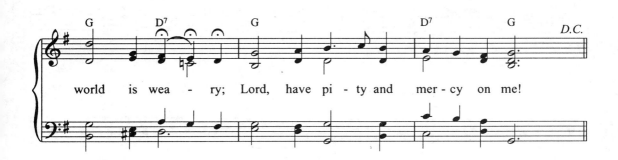

world is wea - ry; Lord, have pi - ty and mer - cy on me!

2. He leaves all his glory behind,
   to be born and to die for mankind,
   with grateful beasts his cradle chooses,
   thankless world his love refuses;
   Lord, have pity and mercy on me!

3. To the manger of Bethlehem come,
   to the Saviour Emmanuel's home;
   the heav'nly hosts above are singing,
   set the Christmas bells a-ringing;
   Lord, have pity and mercy on me!

35 Come now with awe

Words: Timothy Dudley-Smith

Music: Jean Sibelius

FINLANDIA 11 10 11 10 11 10

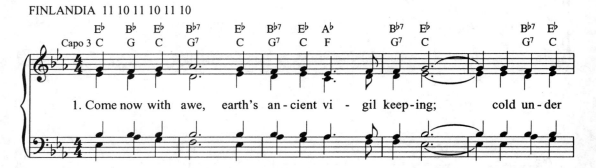

1. Come now with awe, earth's an-cient vi - gil keep-ing; cold un - der

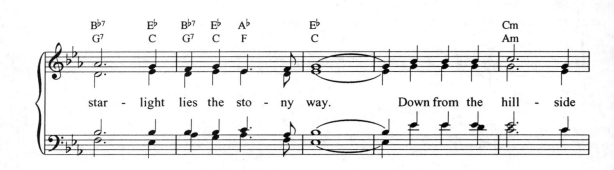

star - light lies the sto - ny way. Down from the hill - side

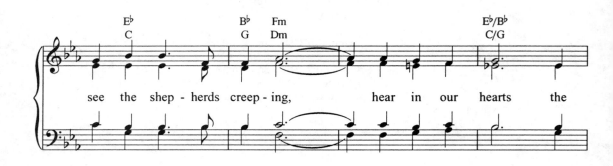

see the shep - herds creep - ing, hear in our hearts the

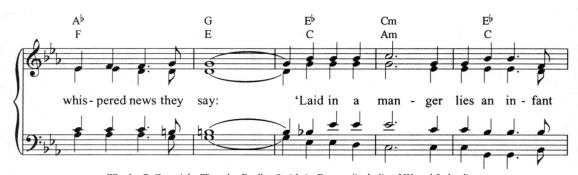

whis - pered news they say: 'Laid in a man - ger lies an in - fant

sleep-ing, Christ our Re - deem - er, born for us to - day.'

2. Come now with joy to worship and adore him;
   hushed in the stillness, wonder and behold,
   Christ in the stable where his mother bore him,
   Christ whom the prophets faithfully foretold:
   High King of ages, low we kneel before him,
   starlight for silver, lantern-light for gold.

3. Come now with faith, the age-long secret guessing,
   hearts rapt in wonder, soul and spirit stirred;
   see in our likeness love beyond expressing,
   all God has spoken, all the prophets heard;
   born for us sinners, bearer of all blessing,
   flesh of our flesh, behold th'eternal Word!

4. Come now with love: beyond our comprehending
   love in its fullness lies in mortal span!
   How should we love, whom Love is so befriending?
   Love rich in mercy since our race began
   now stoops to save us, sighs and sorrows ending,
   Jesus our Saviour, Son of God made man.

36 Come sing the sweet song of the ages
(Song of Immanuel)

Words: Mrs R.N. Turner

Music: Ira D. Sankey
arr. Chris Mitchell

1. Come sing the sweet song of the a - ges — the song of Im-man-u-el sing! There comes thro' the por-tals e-ter-nal an an-them of praise to the King! Then loud let our ca-rols of glad-ness re-e-cho the song of the skies; once more to the ti-dings of glo-ry the earth in its full-ness re-plies.

2. Foretold by the word of the prophets;
   decreed by the wisdom of God;
   we hail the fulfilment of mercy,
   we praise our Redeemer and Lord.

3. The centuries sing of his coming;
   the nations his wonders proclaim;
   and ever increasing in glory,
   we sing of his wonderful name.

4. The song that is sweetest and noblest
   we sing to the Lord we adore;
   and crown him who comes to redeem us –
   Immanuel, King evermore!

37 Come, thou long-expected Jesus

Words: Charles Wesley

Music: John Stainer

TUNE 1: CROSS OF JESUS 87 87

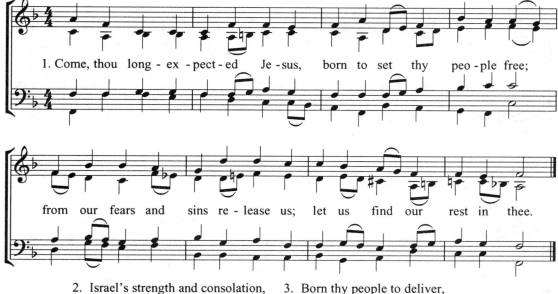

1. Come, thou long-ex-pect-ed Je-sus, born to set thy peo-ple free;

from our fears and sins re-lease us; let us find our rest in thee.

2. Israel's strength and consolation,
   hope of all the earth thou art;
   dear desire of ev'ry nation,
   joy of ev'ry longing heart.

3. Born thy people to deliver,
   born a child and yet a king;
   born to reign in us for ever;
   now thy gracious kingdom bring.

4. By thine own eternal Spirit,
   rule in all our hearts alone:
   by thine all-sufficient merit,
   raise us to thy glorious throne.

Words: Charles Wesley

Music: German melody arr.
Christian Friedrich Witt

TUNE 2: STUTTGART 87 87

1. Come, thou long-ex-pect-ed Je-sus, born to set thy peo-ple free;

from our fears and sins re-lease us; let us find our rest in thee.

38 Come, watch with us

Words: Timothy Dudley-Smith

Music: Phil Burt

1. Come, watch with us this Christ-mas night; our hearts must

tra - vel far to dark - ened hills and hea - vens

bright with star on shi - ning star; to where in

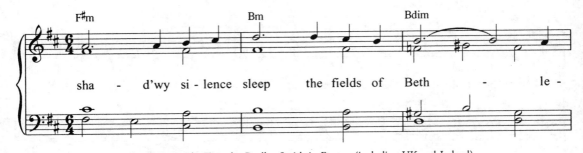

sha - d'wy si - lence sleep the fields of Beth - le -

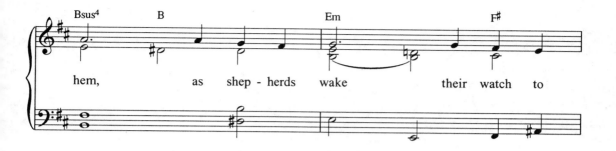

hem,   as   shep - herds   wake   their   watch   to

keep   and   we   will   watch   with   them.

2. Who would not join the angel-songs
   that tell the Saviour's birth?
   The Lord for whom creation longs
   has come at last to earth;
   the fullness of the Father's love
   is ours at Bethlehem,
   while angels throng the skies above
   and we will sing with them.

3. Who would not journey far to share
   the wisdom of the wise,
   and gaze with them in wonder where
   the world's Redeemer lies?
   The Lord of all the lords that are
   is born at Bethlehem,
   and kings shall kneel beneath his star
   and we will bow with them.

4. Lift ev'ry heart the hymn of praise
   that all creation sings;
   the angel host its homage pays,
   the shepherds and the kings.
   For earth and sky with one accord,
   O Child of Bethlehem,
   are come to worship Christ the Lord
   and we will come with them.

39 Crackers and turkeys (Somebody's birthday)

Words and Music: Ian White arr. Donald Thomson

1. Crack-ers and tur-keys and pud-ding and cream, toys in the win-dows that I've ne-ver seen. This is the Christ-mas that ev-'ry-one sees, but Christ-mas means more to me.

Chorus It's some-bo-dy's birth-day I won't for-get, as I o-pen the things that I get. I'll re-mem-ber the inn and the sta-ble so bare, and Je-sus who once lay there. there.

2. Ev'ryone's out shopping late ev'ry night,
   for candles and presents and Christmas tree lights.
   This is the Christmas that ev'ryone sees,
   but Christmas means more to me.

3. Christmas morning, the start of the day,
   there's presents to open and new games to play.
   This is the Christmas that ev'ryone sees,
   but Christmas means more to me.

40 Cradled in a manger

Words: George Stringer Rowe

Music: S.J.P. Dunman

ST WINIFRED 87 87 D

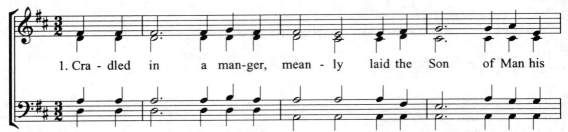

1. Cra - dled in a man-ger, mean - ly laid the Son of Man his

head; sleep-ing his first earth-ly slum - ber where the ox - en had been

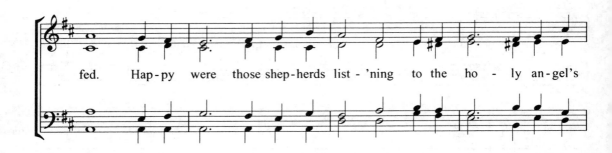

fed. Hap-py were those shep-herds list - 'ning to the ho - ly an-gel's

word; hap-py they with-in that sta - ble, wor-ship-ping their in-fant Lord.

2. Happy all who hear the message
   of his coming from above;
   happier still who hail his coming,
   and with praises greet his love.
   Blessèd Saviour, Christ most holy,
   in a manger thou didst rest;
   canst thou stoop again, yet lower,
   and abide within my breast?

3. Evil things are there before thee;
   in the heart, where they have fed,
   wilt thou pitifully enter,
   Son of Man, and lay thy head?
   Enter, then, O Christ most holy;
   make a Christmas in my heart;
   make a heaven of my manger:
   it is heaven where thou art.

4. And to those who never listened
   to the message of thy birth,
   who have winter, but no Christmas
   bringing them thy peace on earth,
   send to these the joyful tidings;
   by all people, in each home,
   be there heard the Christmas anthem:
   praise to God, the Christ has come!

41 Cradle rocking

Words and Music: Jodi Page Clark
arr. David Peacock

CHRISTMAS LULLABY 87 87 and Refrain

1. Cra - dle rock - ing, cat - tle low - ing, bright star

guid - ing men to see lit - tle Christ - child

in the man - ger, light of all the world to

be: Al - le - lu - ia, ho - ly Child,

ho - san - na in the high - est; glo - ri -

a, Em - man - u - el, ho - san -

To next verse

Last time

- na in the high - est! - est!

2. Mother Mary, watching caref'lly
   by the light of one bright star;
   Bread of heaven, softly sleeping,
   gentle gift of God to man:

3. Who could guess, to see you lie there,
   that you came to bring a sword?
   Prince of peace, born in a manger,
   with a price upon your soul.

4. Do you know – so weak and helpless
   of the grace you bear to us;
   do you dream yet of the kingdom
   you will some day bring to pass?

42 Darkness like a shroud

(Arise, shine!)

Words and Music: Graham Kendrick

2. Children of the light, be clean and pure.
   Rise, you sleepers, Christ will shine on you.
   Take the Spirit's flashing two-edged sword
   and with the faith declare God's mighty word;
   stand up and in his strength be strong.

3. Here among us now Christ the Light
   kindles brighter flames in our trembling hearts.
   Living Word, our lamp, come guide our feet
   as we walk as one in light and peace till
   justice and truth shine like the sun.

4. Like a city bright so let us blaze;
   lights in every street turning night to day.
   And the darkness shall not overcome
   till the fullness of Christ's kingdom comes,
   dawning to God's eternal day.

43 Deck the hall

Words: Traditional

Music: Traditional Welsh melody
arr. Neil Jenkins

NOS GALAN 88 88 with Falas

1. Deck the hall with boughs of hol - ly, fa-la-la-la-la la-la-la-la;

fa - la - la

'tis the sea - son to be jol - ly, fa-la-la-la-la la-la-la-la.

fa - la - la

Don we now our gay ap-pa-rel, fa-la-la-la-la la-la-la-la;

fa-la-la-la-la

troll the an - cient yule-tide ca - rol, fa - la - la la-la-la-la.

2. See the blazing Yule before us,
   fa-la-la-la-la la-la-la-la;
   strike the harp and join the chorus,
   fa-la-la-la-la la-la-la-la.
   Follow me in merry measure,
   fa-la-la-la-la la-la-la-la;
   while I tell the yuletide treasure,
   fa-la-la-la-la la-la-la-la.

3. Fast away the old year passes,
   fa-la-la-la-la la-la-la-la;
   hail the new, ye lads and lasses.
   fa-la-la-la-la la-la-la-la.
   Sing we joyous all together,
   fa-la-la-la-la la-la-la-la;
   heedless of the wind and weather,
   fa-la-la-la-la la-la-la-la.

44 Ding dong, merrily on high!

Words: George Ratcliffe Woodward

Music: Traditional French melody
arr. Charles Wood
Alternative Chorus arr. Colin Hand

BRANSLE DE L'OFFICIAL 77 77 and Refrain

1. Ding dong, mer-ri-ly on high! In heav'n the bells are ring-ing;

ding dong, ve-ri-ly the sky is riv'n with an-gels sing-ing.

Chorus

Glo - - - -

2nd time D.C.

- ri - a, ho-san-na in ex-cel-sis!

An easier setting of the Chorus
Unison

Glo - - - -

2nd time D.C.

- - ri - a, ho - san - na in ex - cel - sis!

2. E'en so here below, below,
   let steeple bells be swungen,
   and io, io, io,
   by priest and people sungen.

3. Pray you, dutifully prime
   your matin chime, ye ringers;
   may you beautifully rhyme
   your evetime song, ye singers.

45 Down from his glory

Words: William E. Booth-Clibborn

Music: Eduardo di Capua

O SOLE MIO 11 12 11 10 and Refrain

1. Down from his glory, e-ver-liv-ing sto - ry,

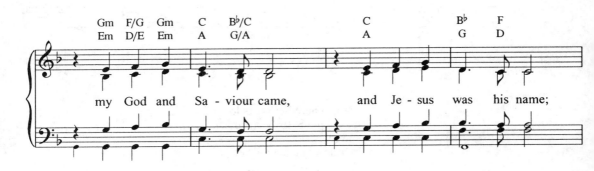

my God and Sa - viour came, and Je - sus was his name;

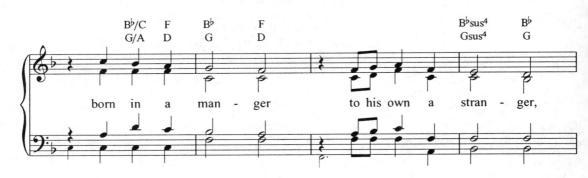

born in a man - ger to his own a stran - ger,

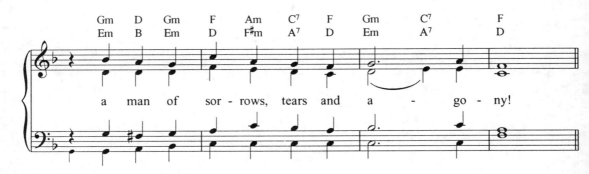

a man of sor - rows, tears and a - go - ny!

2. What condescension, bringing us redemption,
   that in the dead of night, not one faint hope in sight;
   God, gracious, tender, laid aside his splendour,
   stooping to woo, to win, to save my soul.

3. Without reluctance, flesh and blood, his substance,
   he took the form of man, revealed the hidden plan;
   O glorious myst'ry, sacrifice of Calv'ry!
   And now I know he is the great I AM!

46 Earth gave him no welcome

Words and Music: Margaret Clarkson

ST LUKE 11 11 11 11

1. Earth gave him no wel-come, no shel-ter, no home; he
slept in a sta-ble, the inn had no room; no
bed but a man-ger, no pil-low but hay, no
friends but the ox-en who watched where he lay.

2. To seek and to rescue the dying and lost,
   he came to save sinners at infinite cost:
   despised and rejected, forsaken was he;
   earth gave him no welcome but Calvary's tree.

3. Earth gave him no welcome: sin's night has been long;
   but soon comes God's morning all glorious with song:
   then earth shall not see him rejected again;
   triumphant in glory her King comes to reign!

47 Earth lies spellbound

Words and Music: Graham Kendrick

1. Earth lies spellbound in darkness, sin's oppressive night;
yet in Bethlehem hope is burning bright.
Mysteries are unfolding, but the only sign
is a manger bed where a baby cries.

Chorus
Wake up, wake up, it's Christmas morning,

2. Crowding stairways of starlight,
   choirs of angels sing:
   'Glory, glory to God
   in the highest heav'n.
   Peace is stilling the violence,
   hope is rising high,
   God is watching us now
   through a baby's eyes.

3. Weakness shatters the pow'rful,
   meekness shames the proud,
   vain imaginings
   come tumbling down.
   Ancient mercies remembered,
   hungry satisfied,
   lowly, humble hearts
   are lifted high.

48 Emmanuel

Words and Music: Bob McGee
arr. Chris Mitchell

49 Emmanuel, God is with us

Words and Music: Dave Fellingham

With a rocky feel

50 Every Christmas

Words and Music: Mark Johnson and Helen Johnson
arr. Dave Bankhead

1. Ev -'ry Christ - mas we re - mem - ber ba - by Je - sus,

born to the world. For this rea - son each De - cem - ber

is a spe - cial time for us all. true for all time. So

sing a song, ev -'ry-one ce - le - brate,

the time has come, this is a spe-cial date!

time for us all.

CODA

D.S.

2. Ev'ry Christmas we partake in
   fruit and biscuits, pudding and pies.
   But when all the food is eaten
   lies a message true for all time.

3. Ev'ry Christmas we're all busy
   buying gifts and seasonal cards.
   But behind this old tradition
   lies a present come from the past.

4. Ev'ry Christmas we have pleasure
   seeing all the glitter and lights.
   But there is a brighter treasure
   to be found in Jesus Christ.

5. Ev'ry Christmas there are parties
   fun and laughter, music and games.
   But the best place we can start is
   finding Jesus once again.

6. Ev'ry Christmas we remember
   baby Jesus born to the world.
   For this reason each December
   is a special time for us all!

51 For unto us a child is born

Words and Music: David Hadden

Flowing and expressive

1. For un-to us a child is born, un-to
2. And there shall be no end to the
3. For he is the Migh - ty God, he

us a son is giv'n and the gov - ern - ment shall
in - crease of his rule, to the in - crease of his
is the Prince of Peace, the King of kings

be up - on his shoul - ders. For un - to
gov - ern - ment and peace. For he shall
and Lord of lords. All

us a child is born, un - to us a son is giv'n
sit on Da - vid's throne up - hold - ing right - eous-ness,
hon - our to the King, all glo - ry to his name,

and the gov - ern - ment shall be up - on his
our God shall ac - com - plish
for now and e - ver -

shoul - ders.
this.
more.
And he will be called won-der-ful,

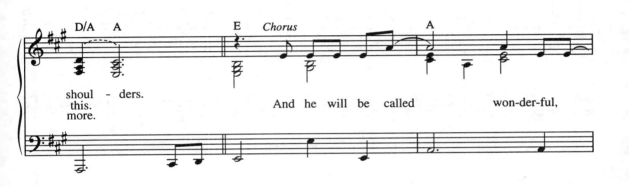

won-der-ful Coun-sel-lor, migh -

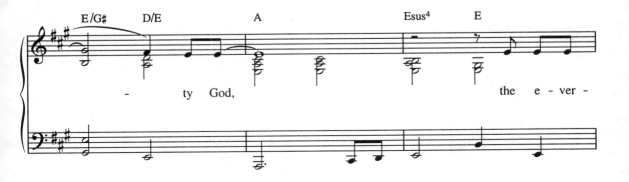

- ty God, the e - ver -

last - ing Fa - ther, Prince of Peace,

migh - ty God.

52 For unto us a child is born

Words: From Isaiah 9

Music: Unknown arr. Phil Burt

53 From heaven above

Words: Michael Perry,
after Martin Luther

Music: Norman Warren

LINDOW LM

Brightly

1. 'From heav'n a - bove I come to bring the
joy - ful news of Christ your king: the ho - ly in - fant
born to - night shall be your hope and your de - light.

2. 'For know that God has kept his word
and sends to you this mighty Lord
to free you from your sin and shame;
the saviour, Jesus, is his name.

3. 'The One by whom the world was made
is in a humble manger laid;
and he to whom the throne was giv'n
now stoops to raise you up to heav'n.'

4. So with the shepherds make your way,
and find in Bethlehem today
the child of peace, the ever-blessed,
your master and your gracious guest.

5. Then bear the news that angels tell
to all the weary world as well;
let human pow'r and pomp and pride
be vanquished at this Christmastide.

6. Sing praises to the Father, Son,
and Holy Spirit – Three in One;
let God made known in Christ our Lord
be worshipped, honoured, and adored.

54 From heaven you came

(The Servant King)

Words and Music: Graham Kendrick

King,   he calls us   now   to fol - low   him,   to bring our

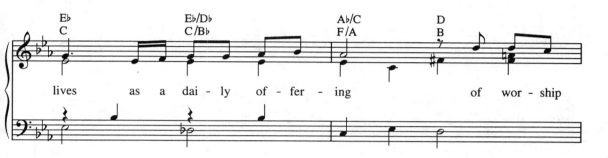

lives   as   a   dai - ly   of - fer - ing   of   wor - ship

To next verse   *Last time*

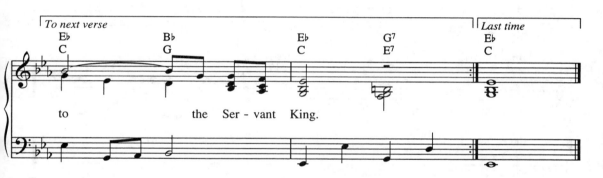

to   the   Ser - vant   King.

2. There in the garden of tears,
   my heavy load he chose to bear;
   his heart with sorrow was torn.
   'Yet not my will but yours,' he said.

3. Come see his hands and his feet,
   the scars that speak of sacrifice,
   hands that flung stars into space,
   to cruel nails surrendered.

4. So let us learn how to serve,
   and in our lives enthrone him;
   each other's needs to prefer,
   for it is Christ we're serving.

55 From the heights of glory

(What a gift)

Words and Music: Susie Hare

2. From a humble stable, to a world of shame,
   the friend of sinners, who calls my name
   brought the love of heaven to the hearts of men
   and it gave lives hope again.

3. From a life, so perfect, to a cruel cross,
   the world's redemption, the Father's loss;
   and the nails were driven and the blood flowed free
   in the hands outstretched for me.

4. From the grave he's risen, ever glorified,
   to take his place at his Father's side;
   and the greatest glory will be ours to own
   when he comes to take us home.

What a hope, what a hope we are given,
sacrifice of the Father for us.
What a song to proclaim: 'He is risen!
King of kings, Lord of lords, Jesus!
King of kings, Lord of lords, Jesus!

56 From the squalor of a borrowed stable

(Immanuel)

Words and Music: Stuart Townend

With a 'celtic' feel

1. From the squa-lor of a bor-rowed sta - ble, by the Spi-rit and a vir - gin's faith; to the an-guish and the shame of scan - dal came the Sa-viour of the hu - man race! But the skies were filled with the praise of heav'n, shep - herds lis - ten as the

an - gels tell of the Gift of God come down to man

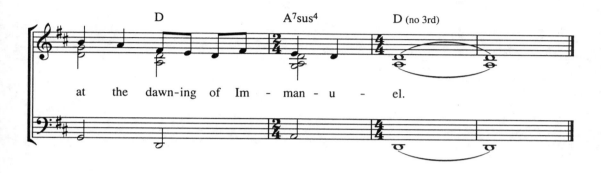

at the dawn-ing of Im - man - u - el.

2. King of heaven now the friend of sinners,
   humble servant in the Father's hands,
   filled with power and the Holy Spirit,
   filled with mercy for the broken man.
   Yes, he walked my road and he felt my pain,
   joys and sorrows that I know so well;
   yet his righteous steps give me hope again –
   I will follow my Immanuel!

3. Through the kisses of a friend's betrayal,
   he was lifted on a cruel cross;
   he was punished for a world's transgressions,
   he was suffering to save the lost.
   He fights for breath, he fights for me,
   loosing sinners from the claims of hell;
   and with a shout our souls are free –
   death defeated by Immanuel!

4. Now he's standing in the place of honour,
   crowned with glory on the highest throne,
   interceding for his own belovèd
   till his Father calls to bring them home!
   Then the skies will part as the trumpet sounds
   hope of heaven or the fear of hell;
   but the Bride will run to her Lover's arms,
   giving glory to Immanuel!

57 Gentle Mary laid her child

Words: Joseph Simpson Cook

Music: *Piae Cantiones*
arr. Chris Mitchell

TEMPUS ADEST FLORIDUM 76 76 D

1. Gentle Mary laid her child lowly in a manger; there he lay, the undefiled, to the world a stranger: such a babe in such a place, can he be the Saviour? Ask the saved of all the race who have found his favour.

2. Angels sang about his birth;
   wise men sought and found him;
   heaven's star shone brightly forth,
   glory all around him:
   shepherds saw the wondrous sight,
   heard the angels singing;
   all the plains were lit that night,
   all the hills were ringing.

3. Gentle Mary laid her child
   lowly in a manger;
   he is still the undefiled,
   but no more a stranger:
   Son of God, of humble birth,
   beautiful the story;
   praise his name in all the earth,
   hail the King of glory!

58 Girls and boys, leave your toys

Words: Malcolm Sargent

Music: Traditional Czech melody
arr. Chris Mitchell

2. On that day, far away, Jesus lay –
    angels were watching round his head.
    Holy child, mother mild, undefiled,
    we sing your praise.
    Alleluia, the church bells ring,
    'Alleluia!' the angels sing,
    alleluia from ev'rything –
    our hearts we raise.

3. Shepherds came at the fame of your name,
    angels their guide to Bethlehem;
    in that place, saw your face filled with grace,
    stood at your door.
    Alleluia, the church bells ring,
    'Alleluia!' the angels sing,
    alleluia from ev'rything –
    love evermore.

59 Glory be to God on high

Words: Charles Wesley alt.

Music: Melody as in John Wesley's
Sacred Harmony

AMSTERDAM 76 76 77 76

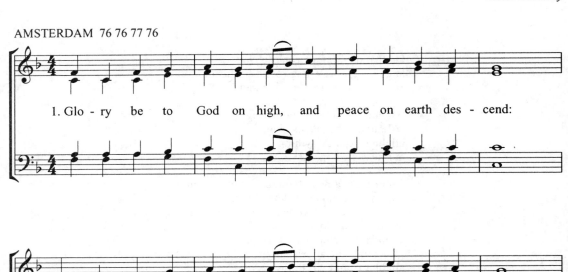

1. Glo - ry be to God on high, and peace on earth des - cend:

God comes down, he bows the sky, and shows him - self our friend:

God the in - vi - si - ble ap - pears: God, the blest, the great 'I Am',

so - journs in this vale of tears, and Je - sus is his name.

2. Him the angels all adored,
   their Maker and their King;
   tidings of their humbled Lord
   they now to mortals bring.
   Emptied of his majesty,
   of his dazzling glories shorn,
   being's source begins to be,
   and God himself is born!

3. See th'eternal Son of God
   a mortal son of man
   dwelling in an earthly clod
   whom heav'n cannot contain!
   Stand amazed, ye heav'ns, at this!
   See the Lord of earth and skies;
   humbled to the dust he is,
   and in a manger lies.

4. We, earth's children, now rejoice,
   the Prince of Peace proclaim;
   with heaven's host lift up our voice,
   and shout Immanuel's name:
   knees and hearts to him we bow;
   of our flesh and of our bone,
   Jesus is our brother now,
   and God is all our own.

60 Glory to God in the highest

Words and Music: Greg Leavers
arr. Chris Mitchell

Glo-ry to God in the high-est, peace

up-on earth, Je - sus Christ has

come to earth; that's why we sing, Je - sus the

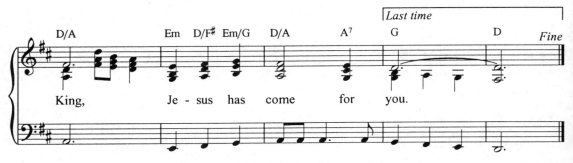

King, Je - sus has come for you.

To continue

| D | D⁷/C | Gm⁷ | C⁷ |

you.   1. The shep-herds who were sit-ting there were

| Fmaj⁷ | B♭maj⁷ | Gm⁷ |

sud - den - ly   filled with fear;   the   dark   night   was

| C⁷ | Gm⁷ | A⁷sus⁴ | A | *D.C.* |

filled with light,   an - gels sing-ing ev - 'ry-where.

2. The next time we hear a song
   of worship from a heav'nly throng,
   will be when Jesus comes again,
   then with triumph we'll all sing:

61 God came among us

Words and Music: Marilyn Baker
arr. David Peacock

Moderate pace (♩ = c.76)

1. God came a-mong us, he be-came a man,
2. He came to serve, to show us how much he cared;
3. Death tried to hold him, but it could not suc-ceed;

be-came a ba - by, though through him the world be - gan.
our joys and sor - rows he so will - ing-ly shared.
he rose a - gain, and now we can be freed.

He came to earth to bring us peace, but
He came to earth to bring us joy, but
He longs to give e - ter - nal life to

where is that peace to - day? It can be found
where is that joy to - day? It can be found
all who will simp - ly re - ceive, yes to all

(Small note vs.1&2)

C/E   Am   Dm/F   Dm   F/G   G⁷

(Small notes vs.2&3)   *(Small note vs.2&3)*

by   those   who will   let   him   di - rect   their

by   those who let   him   wash   their guilt   a -

who   will   o - pen their   hearts   and   just   be -

1st and 2nd times

C   G/B   Am   D/F#

way.

way.

G⁷   C/E   F   G   *Last time*   C

- lieve.

62 God rest you merry, gentlemen

Words: Traditional English

Music: Traditional English melody
arr. John Stainer

GOD REST YOU MERRY 86 86 86 and Refrain

1. God rest you mer - ry, gen - tle - men, let no - thing you dis -

may, re - mem - ber Christ our Sa - viour was born on Christ - mas

day, to save us all from Sa - tan's pow'r when we were gone as -

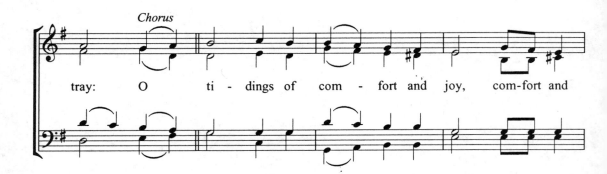

Chorus

tray: O ti - dings of com - fort and joy, com-fort and

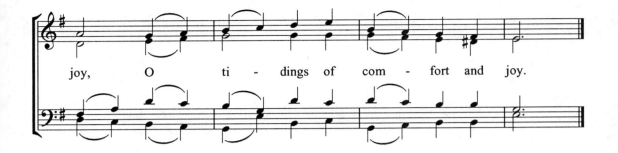

joy, O ti - dings of com - fort and joy.

2. In Bethlehem, in Jewry,
   this blessèd babe was born,
   and laid within a manger,
   upon this blessèd morn;
   the which his mother Mary
   did nothing take in scorn:

3. From God, our heav'nly Father,
   a blessèd angel came,
   and unto certain shepherds,
   brought tidings of the same,
   how that in Bethlehem was born
   the Son of God by name:

4. 'Fear not,' then said the angel,
   'let nothing you affright,
   this day is born a Saviour
   of a pure virgin bright,
   to free all those who trust in him
   from Satan's pow'r and might:'

5. The shepherds at those tidings,
   rejoicèd much in mind,
   and left their flocks a-feeding,
   in tempest, storm and wind:
   and went to Bethlehem straightway,
   the Son of God to find:

6. And when they came to Bethlehem,
   where our dear Saviour lay,
   they found him in a manger,
   where oxen feed on hay;
   his mother Mary kneeling down,
   unto the Lord did pray:

7. Now to the Lord sing praises,
   all you within this place,
   and with true love and brotherhood
   each other now embrace;
   this holy tide of Christmas
   all other doth deface:

63 Good Christian people

Words: Traditional, alt.

Music: Traditional English melody
collected and arr. Ralph Vaughan Williams

SUSSEX CAROL 88 88 88

1. Good Christian people rise and sing to greet the news the angels bring; good Christian people rise and sing to greet the news the angels bring: news of great joy for all the earth, news of our holy saviour's birth!

2. Rejoice and be no longer sad,
   for Christ is born to make us glad;
   rejoice and be no longer sad,
   for Christ is born to make us glad:
   his pow'r will drive away our sin,
   his lowly birth our love shall win.

3. Now in our darkness shines the light
   which made the angels sing that night;
   now in our darkness shines the light
   which made the angels sing that night.
   Glory to God! Goodwill and peace
   be to us all, and never cease!

64 Good Christians all, rejoice

Words: John Mason Neale alt.

Music: 14th century German carol melody
arr. John Stainer

IN DULCI JUBILO Irregular

1. Good Christ - ians all, re - joice with

heart and soul and voice! Give ye heed to

what we say: News! News! Je - sus Christ is born to - day;

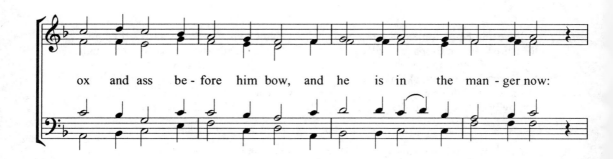

ox and ass be - fore him bow, and he is in the man - ger now:

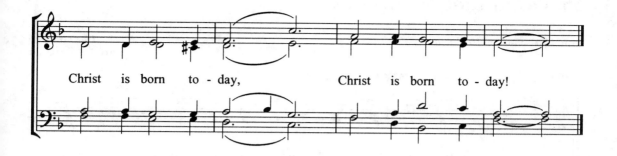

Christ is born to - day, Christ is born to - day!

2. Good Christians all, rejoice
with heart and soul and voice!
Now ye hear of endless bliss:
Joy! Joy! Jesus Christ was born for this.
He hath opened heaven's door,
and we are blest for evermore.
Christ was born for this,
Christ was born for this.

3. Good Christians all, rejoice
with heart and soul and voice!
Now ye need not fear the grave:
Peace! Peace! Jesus Christ was born to save;
calls you one, and calls you all,
to gain his everlasting hall:
Christ was born to save,
Christ was born to save.

65 Good King Wenceslas

Words: John Mason Neale, alt.

Music: *Piae Cantiones*
arr. John Stainer

TEMPUS ADEST FLORIDUM 76 76 D

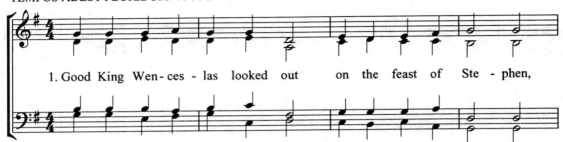

1. Good King Wen - ces - las looked out on the feast of Ste - phen,

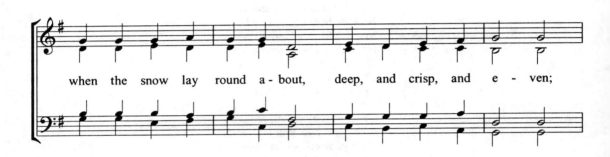

when the snow lay round a - bout, deep, and crisp, and e - ven;

bright - ly shone the moon that night, though the frost was cru - el,

when a poor man came in sight, gath -'ring win - ter fu - el.

2. 'Hither, page, and stand by me,
   if thou know'st it, telling,
   yonder peasant, who is he,
   where and what his dwelling?'
   'Sire, he lives a good league hence,
   underneath the mountain,
   right against the forest fence,
   by Saint Agnes' fountain.'

3. 'Bring me flesh, and bring me wine,
   bring me pine logs hither:
   thou and I will see him dine,
   when we bring them thither.'
   Page and monarch, forth they went,
   forth they went together;
   through the rude wind's wild lament,
   and the bitter weather.

4. 'Sire, the night is darker now,
   and the wind blows stronger;
   fails my heart, I know not how;
   I can go no longer.'
   'Mark my footsteps good, my page;
   tread thou in them boldly:
   thou shalt find the winter's rage
   freeze thy blood less coldly.'

5. In his master's steps he trod,
   where the snow lay dinted;
   heat was in the very sod
   which the Saint had printed.
   Therefore, Christians all, be sure,
   wealth or rank possessing,
   ye who now will bless the poor,
   shall yourselves find blessing.

66 Good news

Words and Music: Graham Kendrick

Brightly, with strength

1. Good news, good news to you we bring, al - le -
lu - ia! News of great joy that an - gels sing,
al - le - lu - ia! Ten-der mer - cy
he has shown us, joy to all the world;

for us God sends his on - ly Son,

al - le - lu - ia!

1, 2.

Esus⁴   E

3.

2. Let
3. Now

2. Let earth's dark shadows fly away,
   Alleluia!
   In Christ has dawned an endless day,
   Alleluia!

3. Now God with us on earth resides,
   Alleluia!
   And heaven's door is open wide,
   Alleluia!

67 Good news of great joy

Words and Music: Phil Chapman
arr. Chris Mitchell

Good news of great joy to all men on

earth. In the old town of Beth - le - hem, our

Sa - viour had his birth. God's mes - sage to all sin - ful men the

same as to the shep - herds then is in these joy - ful

words, 'A Sa - viour born in Da - vid's town' and

at whose name we'll all bow down, for he is Christ the Lord.

68 Go, tell it on the mountain

Words: Traditional

Music: Traditional
arr. Chris Mitchell

Chorus

Go, tell it on the moun - tain, o - ver the hills and ev - 'ry - where; go, tell it on the moun - tain, that Je - sus Christ is born!

1. While shep - herds sat a - watch - ing their si - lent flocks by night, there
   shep - herds feared and trem - bled when, high a - bove the earth, rang

shone through - out the hea - vens   a   great   and   glo - rious
out   the   an - gel   cho - rus   that   hailed   our   Sa - viour's

Chorus

light.
birth.   Go,   tell   it   on   the   moun - tain,

o - ver   the   hills   and   ev - 'ry - where;   go,   tell   it   on   the

To continue   *Last time*

moun - tain, that Je - sus Christ is   born!   2. The   born!

69 Hail to the Lord's anointed

Words: James Montgomery
based on Psalm 72

Music: from a melody in Johann Crüger's *Gesangbuch*
adapted by William Henry Monk

CRÜGER 76 76 D

1. Hail to the Lord's a - noint - ed, great Da - vid's great - er son! Hail, in the time ap - point - ed, his reign on earth be - gun! He comes to break op - pres - sion, to set the cap - tive free; to take a - way trans - gres - sion, and rule in e - qui - ty.

2. He comes with succour speedy
   to those who suffer wrong;
   to help the poor and needy,
   and bid the weak be strong;
   to give them songs for sighing,
   their darkness turn to light,
   whose souls, condemned and dying,
   were precious in his sight.

3. He shall come down like showers
   upon the fruitful earth,
   and love, joy, hope, like flowers,
   spring in his path to birth:
   before him on the mountains
   shall peace the herald go;
   and righteousness in fountains
   from hill to valley flow.

4. Kings shall fall down before him,
   and gold and incense bring;
   all nations shall adore him,
   his praise all people sing;
   to him shall prayer unceasing
   and daily vows ascend;
   his kingdom still increasing,
   a kingdom without end.

5. O'er ev'ry foe victorious,
   he on his throne shall rest,
   from age to age more glorious,
   all-blessing and all-blest;
   the tide of time shall never
   his covenant remove;
   his name shall stand for ever;
   that name to us is love.

70 Hallelu, hallelu, hallelujah

Words and Music: James Wright
arr. Chris Mitchell

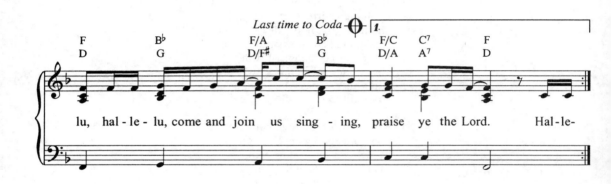

Hal-le- lu, hal-le-lu, hal-le-lu -jah, praise ye the Lord. Hal-le-

lu, hal-le-lu, come and join us sing - ing, praise ye the Lord. Hal-le-

praise ye the Lord. 1. Now Je - sus was born of Ma - ry

in Beth-le-hem, in a dus-ty sta - ble with a low-ly cra - dle

2. Now shepherds were sat on the hillside
   in Bethlehem,
   when a host of angels started singing praises
   in Bethlehem.
   And the night lit up with an awesome sight
   and the shepherds looked amazed,
   but the angel said, 'Please do not fear,
   your King is born this day.'

3. Now wise men travelled a long way
   to Bethlehem,
   from the Orient to the land of Israel
   to Bethlehem.
   And the star shone bright in the sky that night
   to show them where to go,
   so that they may bring gifts to the King,
   myrrh, frankincense and gold.

71 Hallelujah!

Words and Music: Mark and Helen Johnson
arr. Chris Mitchell

With energy

Hal - le - lu - jah! sing hal - le - lu - jah! let's give God the praise,

hal - le - lu - jah! sing hal - le - lu - jah! Christ is born to - day.

day. day.
1. Clap your hands and stamp your feet, (and)
2. God is giv - ing life to us, in

sing   to   God   a - bove,   swing your hips round
Je - sus Christ his   Son,   we   can   come   to

to   the beat,   and ce - le - brate his   love.
know his love,   a   new day has be - gun!

72 Hallelujah, my Father

Words and Music: Tim Cullen

73 Happy day of great rejoicing

Words: Mollie Knight

Music: Ludwig van Beethoven

ODE TO JOY 87 87 D

1. Happy day of great rejoicing! We proclaim a saviour's birth, for a child lies in a manger, Jesus Christ is born on earth. Gladly come, in worship kneeling by the cradle of the Son; sing with joy, ring out your praises, 'Welcome to the Holy One!'

2. Prince of Peace, God's Word incarnate,
   with the poor identified;
   all his riches and his glory
   for love's sake are laid aside.
   Jesus comes to his creation
   loving saviour, God's dear Son:
   sing with joy, ring out your praises,
   'Welcome to the Holy One!'

3. Hear the message of salvation
   Jesus brings to ev'ry race,
   see the infant who embodies
   God's great glory and his grace.
   Purest light will reach dark places
   through the love of Christ the Son:
   sing with joy, ring out your praises,
   'Welcome to the Holy One!'

74 Hark, the glad sound!

Words: Philip Doddridge
based on Luke 4:18-19

Music: Thomas Ravenscroft,
Psalms

BRISTOL CM

1. Hark, the glad sound! the Sa - viour comes, the Sa - viour pro - mised

long: let ev - 'ry heart pre - pare a throne, and ev - 'ry voice a song.

2. He comes, the pris'ners to release
   in Satan's bondage held;
   the gates of brass before him burst,
   the iron fetters yield.

3. He comes, the broken heart to bind,
   the bleeding soul to cure,
   and with the treasures of his grace
   to bless the humble poor.

4. Our glad hosannas, Prince of Peace,
   thy welcome shall proclaim;
   and heav'n's eternal arches ring
   with thy belovèd name.

A lower setting

1. Hark, the glad sound! the Sa - viour comes, the Sa - viour pro - mised long: let ev - 'ry heart pre - pare a throne, and ev - 'ry voice a song.

75 Hark, the herald-angels sing

Words: Charles Wesley, George Whitefield,
Martin Madan and others, alt.

Music: adapted from Felix Mendelssohn
by William Hayman Cummings

MENDELSSOHN 77 77 D and Refrain

hem.' Hark, the he-rald-an-gels sing glo - ry to the new-born King.

2. Christ, by highest heav'n adored,
Christ, the everlasting Lord,
late in time behold him come,
offspring of a virgin's womb!
Veiled in flesh the Godhead see,
hail, th'incarnate Deity!
Pleased as man with us to dwell,
Jesus, our Emmanuel.

3. Hail, the heav'n-born Prince of Peace!
Hail, the Sun of Righteousness!
Light and life to all he brings,
ris'n with healing in his wings;
mild he lays his glory by,
born that we no more may die,
born to raise us from the earth,
born to give us second birth.

76 Hark to the story

(*Sing Hosannas*)

Words: Alta C. Faircloth

Music: Polish carol
arr. Alta C. Faircloth

McCRAY 55 6 55 6 and Refrain

1. Hark to the sto-ry an-gels are tell-ing of the birth of Je-sus, born in a man-ger mid cat-tle low-ly is the babe most ho-ly.

Chorus

Sing, all you an-gels, sing, all you shep-herds! Sing to the lit-tle babe in the man-ger; sing a soft ho-san-na, sing a loud ho-san-na, Je-sus Christ is born to-day.

2. Shepherds a-keeping
   watch on the hillside
   heard the wondrous story,
   knelt down in wonder,
   gazed at the glory
   suddenly appearing.

3. Come, all you people,
   come to the manger,
   worship and adore him;
   sing as the angels,
   kneel as the shepherds,
   to the Christ our Saviour.

77 Hear the sound of people singing
(The Christmas Child)

Words and Music: Graham Kendrick

1. Hear the sound of peo - ple sing - ing, all the bells are
   In the streets the lights are glow - ing, but there is no

ring - ing for the Christ - mas Child.
know - ing of the Christ - mas Child.

𝄋 Chorus

Oh, let this Child be born in your heart,

oh, let this Child be born in your heart, to -

2. Will our wars go on for ever,
   and will peace be never
   at Christmastime?
   If we keep him in the manger
   then there is no danger
   from the Christmas Child.

78 Heaven invites you to a party

Words and Music: Graham Kendrick

Joyful, with a strong rhythm

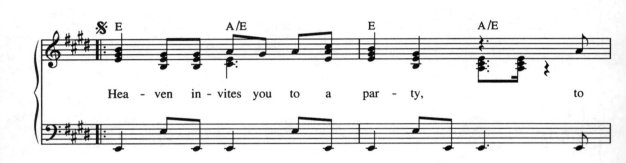

Hea - ven in - vites you to a par - ty, to

ce - le - brate the birth of a Son;

an - gels re - joic - ing in the star - light, sing - ing

79 He came in love to bring hope

Words and Music: Margaret Carpenter
arr. Dave Bankhead

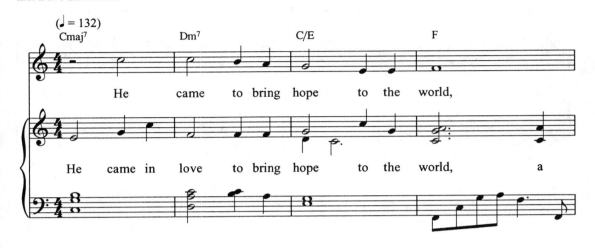

He came to bring hope to the world,
He came in love to bring hope to the world, a

a world that lost its way;
world that had lost its way;

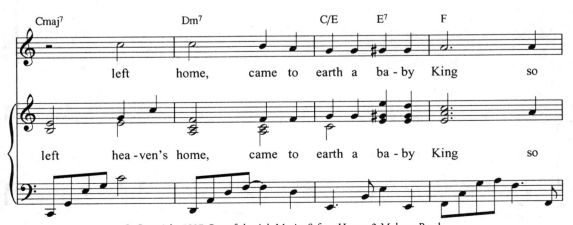

left home, came to earth a ba-by King so
left hea-ven's home, came to earth a ba-by King so

now, ev - 'ry Christ-mas we can glad - ly sing:

now, ev - 'ry Christ-mas we can glad - ly sing: Let the

Let the bells ring, let the bells ring,

bells ring out, let the peo - ple shout songs of

joy to the King, the King of kings.

joy to the King, the King of kings. Let the

80 Hee, haw! Hee, haw! *(The donkey's Christmas carol)*

Words: Michael Forster

Music: Noel Rawsthorne

not his fault at all, but his par-ents should res-pect a don-key's feed-ing-stall!

2. After all that journey,
   with my heavy load,
   did I ever once complain about the dreadful road?
   I can cope with backache,
   and these swollen feet.
   All I ask is some respect, and one square meal to eat.

3. 'Be prepared,' I told them,
   'better book ahead.'
   Joseph said, 'Don't be an ass,' and took a chance instead.
   Now they've pinched my bedroom,
   people are so rude!
   I can cope with that, but not a baby in my food!

81 He is born, our Lord and Saviour

Words and Music: Jimmy Owens

2. He who is from everlasting
   now becomes th'incarnate Word;
   he whose name endures for ever
   now is born the Son of God:
   born to bear our griefs and sorrows,
   born to banish hate and strife;
   born to bear the sin of many,
   born to give eternal life!

3. Hail, the Holy One of Israel,
   chosen heir to David's throne;
   hail the brightness of his rising –
   to his light the Gentiles come:
   plunderer of Satan's kingdom,
   downfall of his evil pow'r;
   rescuer of all his people,
   conqueror in death's dark hour!

4. He shall rule with righteous judgement,
   and his godly rule extend;
   governor among the nations,
   his great kingdom has no end:
   he shall reign, the King of glory,
   higher than the kings of earth –
   alleluia, alleluia!
   Praise we now his holy birth!

82 Here we come to Bethlehem

Words and Music: Emma F. Bush
arr. Chris Mitchell

1. Here we come to Beth-le-hem, here we come to Beth-le-hem, here we come to Beth-le-hem to see the ba-by Je - sus.

2. Here we see the shepherds kneel,
   here we see the shepherds kneel,
   here we see the shepherds kneel
   before the baby Jesus.

3. Here the wise men bring their gifts,
   here the wise men bring their gifts,
   here the wise men bring their gifts
   to give the baby Jesus.

4. We will sing on Christmas Day,
   we will sing on Christmas Day,
   we will sing on Christmas Day
   praise to the baby Jesus.

83 His name, his name

Words: Unknown

Music: Jean Sibelius

84 Holy child

Words: Timothy Dudley-Smith

Music: Michael Baughen
arr. Phil Burt

Tenderly

1. Ho-ly child, how still you lie! safe the man-ger, soft the

hay; faint up-on the east-ern sky breaks the

dawn of Christ-mas Day. *Fine* 2. Ho-ly child, whose birth-day

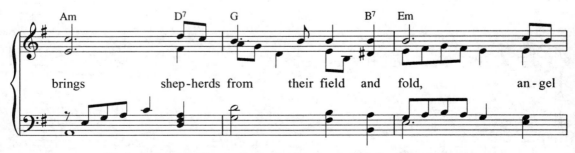

brings shep-herds from their field and fold, an-gel

choirs and east-ern kings, myrrh and frank-in-cense and gold:

2. Holy child, whose birthday brings
   shepherds from their field and fold,
   angel choirs and eastern kings,
   myrrh and frankincense and gold:

3. Holy child, what gift of grace
   from the Father freely willed!
   In your infant form we trace
   all God's promises fulfilled.

4. Holy child, whose human years
   span like ours delight and pain;
   one in human joys and tears,
   one in all but sin and stain:

5. Holy child, so far from home,
   all the lost to seek and save,
   to what dreadful death you come,
   to what dark and silent grave.

6. Holy child, before whose name
   pow'rs of darkness faint and fall;
   conquered death and sin and shame,
   Jesus Christ is Lord of all.

7. Holy child, how still you lie!
   safe the manger, soft the hay;
   clear upon the eastern sky
   breaks the dawn of Christmas Day.

85 Holy, holy Lord

Words and Music: Philip Warren

Gently

Chorus

Holy, holy Lord,

ho - ly, ho - ly Lord,

God of pow'r and love.

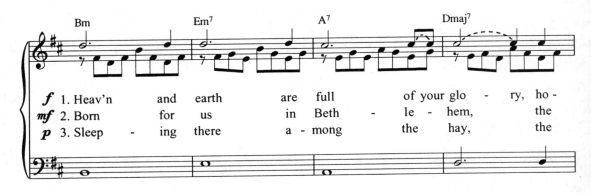

f 1. Heav'n and earth are full of your glo - ry, ho -
mf 2. Born for us in Beth - le - hem, the
p 3. Sleep - ing there a - mong the hay, the

san - na in the high - est.
Sa - viour of the world.
Prince of Peace has come.

Descant

f 4. Heav'n and earth are full of your

Bm   Em⁷   A⁷

f 4. Heav'n and earth are full of your

glo - ry, ho - san - na in the

Dmaj⁷   Bm   E⁷

glo - ry, ho - san - na in the

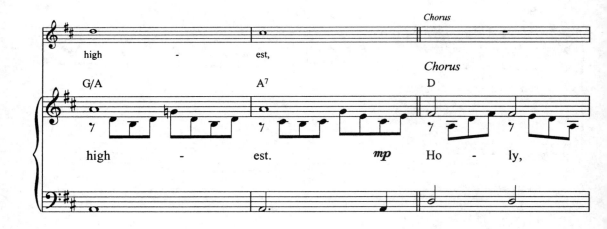

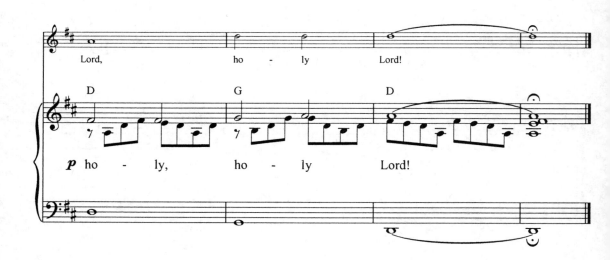

86 How far is it to Bethlehem?

Words: Frances Chesterton

Music: Traditional English carol
arr. Neil Jenkins

STOWEY 74 74 D

1. How far is it to Beth - le - hem? Not ve - ry far? Shall
3. May we stroke the crea - tures there, ox, ass or sheep? May
5. Great kings have pre - cious gifts, and we have naught. Our

we find the sta - ble room lit by a star? 2. Can
we peep like them and see Je - sus a - sleep? 4. If
smiles and our tears are all we have brought. 6. For

(Small notes v.7)

we see the lit - tle child, is he with - in? If
we touch his ti - ny hand, will he a - wake? Will,
all wea - ry child - ren Ma - ry must weep, so,
7. God's in his mo - ther's arms; babes in the byre

(Small notes v.7)

D.S. after v.6
(Small notes v.6)

we lift the wood - en latch, may we go in?
he know we've come so far, just for his sake?
here on his bed of straw, sleep, child - ren, sleep.
sleep, as they sleep who find their heart's de - sire.

(Small notes v.6)

87 Immanuel, God is with us

Words and Music: Graham Kendrick

wis - dom, the migh - ty God

on a dus-ty road. Ev - er-last - ing Fa-

- ther, a friend of sin - ners,

the Prince of Peace in a cat-tle stall.

D.C. al Fine

2. He was despised and rejected,
a man of sorrows acquainted with grief.
From him we turned and hid our faces;
he was despised, him we did not esteem.

3. But he was wounded for our transgressions,
he was bruised for our iniquities.
On him was the punishment that made us whole,
and by his stripes we are healed.

4. He was oppressed, he was afflicted,
and yet he opened not his mouth.
Like a lamb that is led to the slaughter,
like a sheep before his shearers he did not speak.

Suggested order: chorus, v.1, v.2, chorus, v.3, v.4, chorus

88 Immanuel, O Immanuel

Words and Music: Graham Kendrick

89 In a very ordinary stable

(*Look no further*)

Words and Music: Mark and Helen Johnson
arr. Chris Mitchell

1. In a ve-ry or-di-na-ry sta-ble long a-

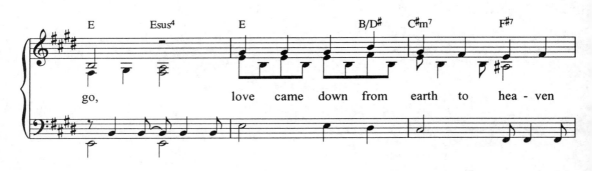

go, love came down from earth to hea-ven

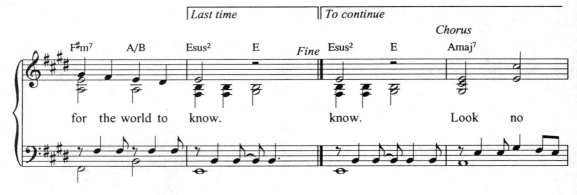

Last time | *To continue* | *Chorus*

Fine

for the world to know. know. Look no

fur-ther, love is here, to dis-

co - ver through the years.

Love that com - forts, love that gives,

love that shows us how to live.

2. On a very cold and lonely hillside long ago,
   love reached out in pure forgiveness,
   for the world to know.

Verse 3 Instrumental

4. In this very moment as in ages long ago,
   love is here today, for ever,
   for the world to know.

90 Infant holy, infant lowly

Words: Traditional Polish
trans. Edith Margaret Gellibrand Reed

Music: Traditional Polish melody
arr. Colin Hand

WZLOBIE LEZY 87 87 88 77

1. In - fant ho - ly, in - fant low - ly, for his bed a cat - tle stall; ox - en low - ing, lit - tle know - ing Christ the babe is Lord of all. Swift are wing - ing an - gels sing - ing, no - wells ring - ing, ti - dings bring - ing, Christ the babe is Lord of all, Christ the babe is Lord of all.

2. Flocks were sleeping, shepherds keeping
   vigil till the morning new;
   saw the glory, heard the story,
   tidings of a gospel true.
   Thus rejoicing, free from sorrow,
   praises voicing, greet the morrow,
   Christ the babe was born for you,
   Christ the babe was born for you.

91 In the bleak midwinter

Words: Christina Georgina Rossetti

Music: Gustav Holst

CRANHAM Irregular

1. In the bleak mid-win-ter frost-y wind made moan, earth stood hard as ir - on, wa-ter like a stone; snow had fall - en, snow on snow, snow on snow, in the bleak mid-win-ter, long a-go.

2. Our God, heav'n cannot hold him
   nor earth sustain;
   heav'n and earth shall flee away
   when he comes to reign.
   In the bleak midwinter
   a stable-place sufficed
   the Lord God almighty,
   Jesus Christ.

3. Enough for him, whom cherubim
   worship night and day,
   a breastful of milk
   and a mangerful of hay:
   enough for him, whom angels
   fall down before,
   the ox and ass and camel
   which adore.

4. Angels and archangels
   may have gathered there,
   cherubim and seraphim
   thronged the air;
   but only his mother
   in her maiden bliss
   worshipped the belovèd
   with a kiss.

5. What can I give him,
   poor as I am?
   If I were a shepherd
   I would bring a lamb;
   if I were a wise man
   I would do my part,
   yet what I can I give him:
   give my heart.

92 In the firelight

(Beautiful night)

Words and Music: Graham Kendrick

1. In the fire-light wait-ing, watch-ing through the dark night, when an-gel voi-ces split the si-lent night; who would be-lieve this sight? Eyes of won-der, as an-gel fa-ces lit a strange light, shep-herd fa-ces hid from glo-ry bright; who would be-lieve this beau-ti-ful

93 Into darkness light has broken

Words: David Mowbray

Music: Francis Jackson

EAST ACKLAM 84 84 888 4

1. In-to dark-ness light has bro-ken, Christ has been born!
Out of si-lence God has spo-ken; Christ has been born!
Prince of Peace, the na-tions greet him, thrones and pow'rs can-not de-feat him:
sing for joy and come to meet him. Christ has been born!

2. For to us a son is given,
Christ has been born!
Treasured gift to earth from heaven;
Christ has been born!
Wondrous counsellor to guide us,
judge when justice is denied us,
everlasting God beside us.
Christ has been born!

3. Promised child – we tell the story –
Christ has been born!
Son of David, Israel's glory:
Christ has been born!
In this child our God has sought us,
wisdom from on high has taught us,
hope and healing now has brought us.
Christ has been born!

94 I saw three ships

Words: Taken from William Sandys'
Christmas Carols, Ancient and Modern

Music: Traditional English
arr. Neil Jenkins

1. I saw three ships come sail-ing in, on Christ-mas Day, on Christ-mas Day. I

saw three ships come sail-ing in, on Christ-mas Day in the morn - ing. 2. And

what was in those ships all three, on Christ-mas Day, on Christ-mas Day? And

what was in those ships all three, on Christ-mas Day in the morn - ing?

The solo can be taken by either a male or female voice.

3. Our Saviour Christ and his Lady,
   on Christmas Day, on Christmas Day.
   Our Saviour Christ and his Lady,
   on Christmas Day in the morning.

4. Pray, whither sailed those ships all three,
   on Christmas Day, on Christmas Day?
   Pray, whither sailed those ships all three,
   on Christmas Day in the morning?

5. O they sailed into Bethlehem,
   on Christmas Day, on Christmas Day.
   O they sailed into Bethlehem,
   on Christmas Day in the morning.

6. And all the bells on earth shall ring,
   on Christmas Day, on Christmas Day.
   And all the bells on earth shall ring,
   on Christmas Day in the morning.

95 It came upon the midnight clear

Words: Edmund Hamilton Sears, alt.

Music: Traditional English melody
arr. Arthur Seymour Sullivan

2. Still through the cloven skies they come,
   with peaceful wings unfurled;
   and still their heav'nly music floats
   o'er all the weary world:
   above its sad and lowly plains
   they bend on hov'ring wing;
   and ever o'er its Babel-sounds
   the blessèd angels sing.

3. Yet with the woes of sin and strife
   the world has suffered long;
   beneath the angel-strain have rolled
   two thousand years of wrong;
   and warring humankind hears not
   the love-song which they bring:
   O hush the noise of mortal strife,
   and hear the angels sing!

4. And ye, beneath life's crushing load,
   whose forms are bending low,
   who toil along the climbing way
   with painful steps and slow:
   look now! for glad and golden hours
   come swiftly on the wing;
   O rest beside the weary road,
   and hear the angels sing.

5. For lo, the days are hast'ning on,
   by prophets seen of old,
   when with the ever-circling years
   comes round the age of gold;
   when peace shall over all the earth
   its ancient splendours fling,
   and all the world give back the song
   which now the angels sing.

96 It's the time

Words and Music: James Wright
arr. Chris Mitchell

It's the time to start the fes - tive mu - sic, it's the time to lift your voice and sing. It's the time of praise and ce - le - bra - tion, it's the birth-day of Je - sus Christ the King. Je - sus Christ the King.

1. Ev - 'ry - bo - dy praise him for send - ing us the Son from the Fa-ther's glo - ry to
2. Ev - 'ry - bo - dy praise him for Christ has come to earth, ev - 'ry-bo-dy praise him on

97 It was on a starry night

(A starry night)

Words and Music: Joy Webb
arr. Chris Mitchell

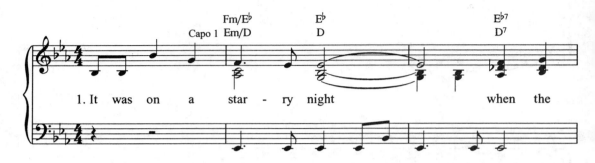

1. It was on a star-ry night when the

hills were bright. Earth lay sleep-ing,

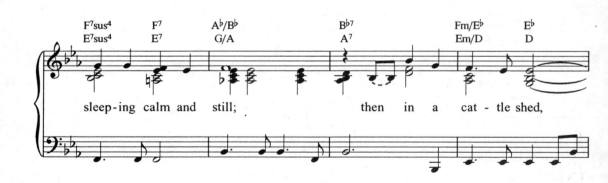

sleep-ing calm and still; then in a cat-tle shed,

in a man-ger bed a boy was born,

King of all the world. And all the an-gels sang for him,

the bells of hea-ven rang for him; for a boy was

born, King of all the world.

On a star-ry night, on a star-ry night.

2. Soon the shepherds came that way,
where the baby lay,
and were kneeling,
kneeling by his side.
And their hearts believed again,
for the peace of men;
for a boy was born,
King of all the world.

98 I wonder as I wander

Words: Appalachian carol

Music: Traditional Appalachian, collected
and arranged by John Jacob Niles

Tenderly
Introduction and link
Harmony

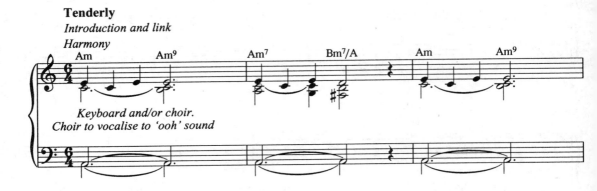

Keyboard and/or choir.
Choir to vocalise to 'ooh' sound

Solo (or Unison) *

1.I won-der as I wan-der, out un-der the sky, why

(ooh) ah

Je-sus the sa-viour came down from on high for us low-ly peo-ple to

(ah)

Verse may be performed as:
 either (1) Unison or Solo;
  or (2) Solo and 2-part chpoir (SA);
  or (3) Solo and 4-part choir (optional 'a cappella')

2. When Jesus was born it was in a cow's stall –
   came angels and shepherds and wise men and all,
   and from the high heaven a star's light did fall,
   the wonderful promise of God to recall.

3. If Jesus had wanted for any one thing –
   a star in the sky, or a bird on the wing,
   or all of God's angels in heaven to sing –
   he surely could have it, for he was the king.

4. I wonder as I wander, out under the sky,
   why Jesus the saviour came down from on high
   for us lowly people to suffer and die –
   I wonder as I wander, out under the sky.

99 Jesus, baby Jesus

Words and Music: Roger Jones from *Stargazers*
arr. Chris Mitchell

as you're sleep - ing, Sa - viour, are you

mine? Je - sus, though a ba - by,

Je - sus, you're di - vine.

100 Jesus born in Bethlehem *(The Holy Gospel)*

Words and Music: J. Macpherson

2. Jesus called disciples too,
   twelve of them in all. *(x2)*
   That's the Holy Gospel,
   good news for one and all.
   Jesus called disciples too,
   twelve of them in all.

3. Jesus healed the sick and lame,
   when in faith they called . . .

4. Jesus sailed upon the sea,
   calmed the raging storm . . .

5. Jesus died upon the cross,
   carried the sins of all . . .

6. Jesus rose to life again,
   he is our living Lord . . .

101 Jesus Christ the Lord is born

Words: Michael Perry
from the German

Music: From *Piae Cantiones*
arr. Chris Mitchell

PUER NOBIS 76 77

1. Je-sus Christ the Lord is born, all the bells are ring-ing! An-gels greet the Ho-ly One and shep-herds hear them sing - ing, and shep-herds hear them sing - ing.

2. 'Go to Bethlehem today,
   find your King and Saviour:
   glory be to God on high,
   to earth his peace and favour,
   to earth his peace and favour!'

3. Held within a cattle stall,
   loved by love maternal,
   see the Master of us all,
   our Lord of lords eternal,
   our Lord of lords eternal.

4. Soon shall come the wise men three,
   rousing Herod's anger;
   mothers' hearts shall broken be
   and Mary's son in danger,
   and Mary's son in danger.

5. Death from life and life from death,
   our salvation's story;
   let all living things give breath
   to Christmas songs of glory,
   to Christmas songs of glory.

102 Jesus, hope of every nation

Words and Music: Michael Perry
arr. David Peacock

EVERSLEY 87 87

Flowing

1. Je - sus, hope of ev - 'ry na - tion,
2. Saints by faith on God de - pend - ing
3. Look, he comes! – the long - a - wait - ed

light of heav'n up - on our way;
wait to see Mes - si - ah born;
Christ, re - deem - er, liv - ing Word;

pro - mise of the world's sal - va - tion,
sin's op - pres - sive night is end - ing
hope and faith are vin - di - ca - ted

Verses 1 and 2 ‖ *Verse 3*

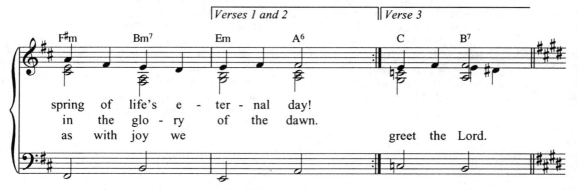

spring of life's e - ter - nal day!
in the glo - ry of the dawn.
as with joy we greet the Lord.

103 Jesus, my Saviour

(Seeking for me!)

Words: Sankey's *Sacred Songs and Solos*

Music: Unknown
arr. Chris Mitchell

SEEKING FOR ME 10 10 10 6 and Refrain

1. Je - sus, my Sa - viour, to Beth - le - hem came, born in a man - ger to

sor - row and shame; oh, it was won - der - ful – blest be his name!

Chorus

Seek-ing for me, for me! Seek-ing for me, for me!
(Seek-ing for me!)

Seek-ing for me, for me! Oh, it was won - der - ful –
(Seek-ing for me!)

© Copyright Control.

blest be his name! Seek-ing for me, for me!

2. Jesus, my Saviour, on Calvary's tree,
   paid the great debt, and my soul he set free;
   oh, it was wonderful – how could it be?
   dying for me, for me!

   Chorus
   Dying for me! Dying for me!
   Oh, it was wonderful – how could it be?
   Dying for me, for me!

3. Jesus, my Saviour, the same as of old,
   while I was wand'ring afar from the fold,
   gently and long did he plead with my soul,
   calling for me, for me!

   Chorus
   Calling for me! Calling for me!
   Gently and long did he plead with my soul,
   calling for me, for me.

4. Jesus, my Saviour, shall come from on high –
   sweet is the promise as weary years fly;
   oh, I shall see him descend from the sky,
   coming for me, for me!

   Chorus
   Coming for me! Coming for me!
   Oh, I shall see him descend from the sky,
   coming for me, for me!

104 Jesus, name above all names

Words and Music: Naida Hearn

105 Journey to Bethlehem

Words: Michael Perry

Music: Roger Mayor

STONY BROOK 10 8 D

2. Come with your presents of honour and love,
   honour and love, honour and love;
   this is the birthday of hope from above,
   hope from above, hope from above.

3. Come with your sorrow for wrongs you have done,
   wrongs you have done, wrongs you have done;
   find your forgiveness in God's only Son,
   God's only Son, God's only Son.

4. Come with your praises and joyfully sing,
   joyfully sing, joyfully sing;
   journey to Bethlehem, worship your king,
   worship your king, worship your king!

106 Joyful, joyful, we adore thee

Words: Henry van Dyke

Music: Ludwig van Beethoven
adapted by Edward Hodges

2. All thy works with joy surround thee,
   earth and heav'n reflect thy rays.
   Stars and angels sing around thee,
   centre of unbroken praise.
   Field and forest, vale and mountain,
   flow'ry meadow, flashing sea,
   chanting bird and flowing fountain
   call us to rejoice in thee!

3. Thou art giving and forgiving,
   ever blessing, ever blest,
   wellspring of the joy of living,
   ocean depth of happy rest!
   Thou our Father, Christ our brother,
   all who live in love are thine.
   Teach us how to love each other;
   lift us to the joy divine!

4. Mortals, join the mighty chorus
   which the morning stars began;
   love divine is reigning o'er us,
   leading us with mercy's hand.
   Ever singing, march we onward,
   victors in the midst of strife.
   Joyful music leads us sunward
   in the triumph-song of life!

107 Joy to all the world

(Anno Domini)

Words and Music: Graham Kendrick
arr. Jonathan Savage

the chor - us. 3. Go through all the earth, sing the new song, shout from East to West, Here is your God.

108 Joy to the world

Words: Isaac Watts, alt.

Music: George Frideric Handel

ANTIOCH CM

1. Joy to the world! The Lord is come; let earth re-ceive her King; let ev-'ry heart pre-pare him room and heav'n and na-ture sing, and heav'n and na-ture sing, and heav'n, and heav'n and na-ture sing!

2. Joy to the earth! The Saviour reigns;
   let us our songs employ;
   while fields and floods, rocks, hills and plains
   repeat the sounding joy,
   repeat the sounding joy,
   repeat, repeat the sounding joy.

3. He rules the world with truth and grace,
   and makes the nations prove
   the glories of his righteousness,
   and wonders of his love,
   and wonders of his love,
   and wonders, wonders of his love.

109 Kings came riding

Words and Music: Joan Lawton

With increasing pace

Chime bars/Descant recorder

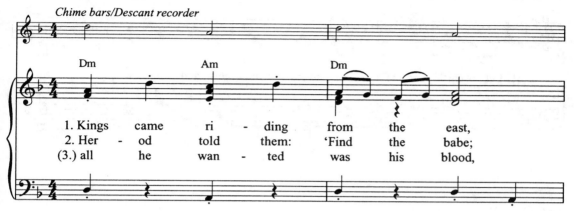

1. Kings came ri - ding from the east,
2. Her - od told them: 'Find the babe;
(3.) all he wan - ted was his blood,

search - ing for the Prince of Peace; then King Her - od,
come and tell me where he's laid; I will go there,
have this in - fant gone for good. Quick - ly ri - ding

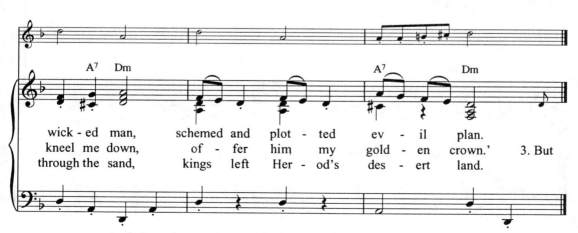

wick - ed man, schemed and plot - ted ev - il plan.
kneel me down, of - fer him my gold - en crown.' 3. But
through the sand, kings left Her - od's des - ert land.

110 Let earth and heaven combine

Words: Charles Wesley

Music: *Supplement to Wesley's Hymns*

MILLENNIUM 66 66 88

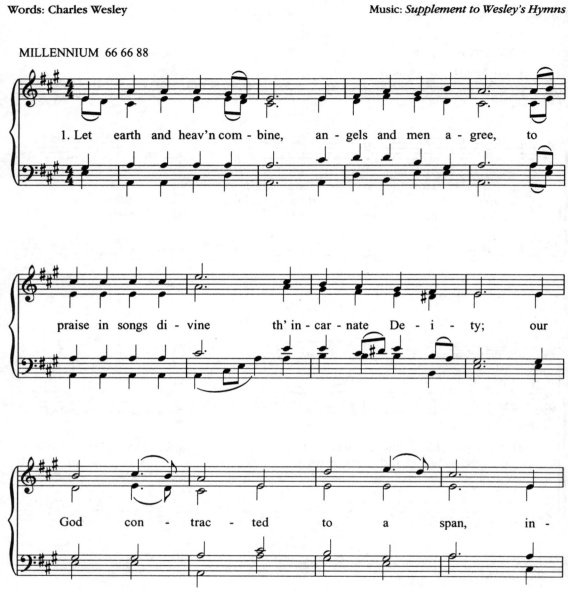

1. Let earth and heav'n com - bine, an - gels and men a - gree, to praise in songs di - vine th' in - car - nate De - i - ty; our God con - trac - ted to a span, in -

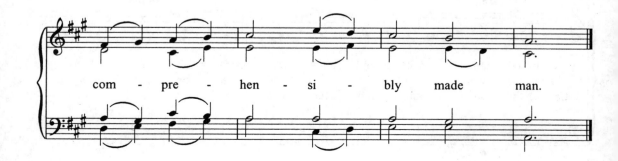

com - pre - hen - si - bly made man.

2. He laid his glory by,
   he wrapped him in our clay;
   unmarked by human eye,
   the latent Godhead lay;
   infant of days he here became,
   and bore the mild Immanuel's name.

3. Unsearchable the love
   that hath the Saviour brought;
   the grace is far above
   mankind's or angel's thought:
   suffice for us that God, we know,
   our God, is manifest below.

4. He deigns in flesh to appear,
   widest extremes to join;
   to bring our vileness near,
   and make us all divine:
   and we the life of God shall know,
   for God is manifest below.

5. Made perfect first in love,
   and sanctified by grace,
   we shall from earth remove,
   and see his glorious face:
   then shall his love be fully showed,
   and man shall then be lost in God.

111 Let me tell you about a baby (Christmas calypso)

Words and Music: Mark and Helen Johnson
arr. Donald Thomson

1. Let me tell you a - bout a ba - by, and his fa - mi - ly.

It is writ - ten down in the Bi - ble

so you might be - lieve. Ma - ny men had told

of his com - ing, down through his - to - ry.

Now the time had come for ful - fil - ment of their pro - phe - cy.

2. There was once a young girl called Mary,
   only in her teens.
   She was visited by an angel,
   sent to Galilee.
   And he told her she'd have a baby,
   how she couldn't see.
   Yet it was her will to obey him,
   so it was agreed.

3. Well, in those days Caesar Augustus
   issued a decree,
   and so Mary went with her husband
   where they had to be.
   There was nowhere else but a stable,
   where they both could sleep.
   It was there that she had her baby,
   born for you and me.

112 Let there be singing

Words and Music: James Wright
arr. Chris Mitchell

Let there be sing - ing, songs of re - joic - ing;
Let ev - 'ry na - tion sing of God's sal - va - tion;

let there be joy through - out the earth.
this is the sea - son

to re - joice. From hea - ven to earth you
earth to

came, the Son of God to reign. God's gift of
dwell, Je - sus, Em - man - u - el. God's gift of

e - ver - last - ing love. From hea - ven to
e - ver -

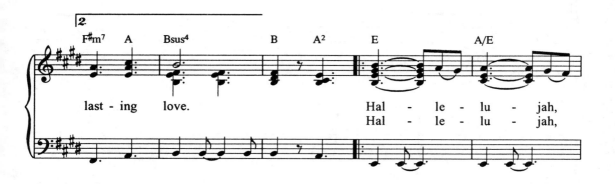

last - ing love. Hal - le - lu - jah,
Hal - le - lu - jah,

hal - le - lu - jah, God with us has
hal - le - lu - jah, God with us, Em -

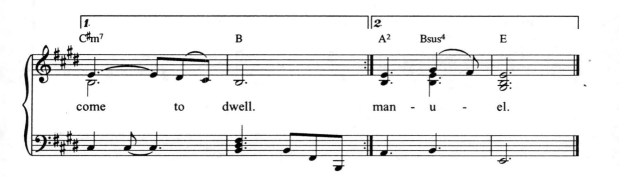

come to dwell. man - u - el.

113 Light shining in the darkness

Words: Anne Johnson

Music: Paul Herrington and David Stone
arr. David Peacock

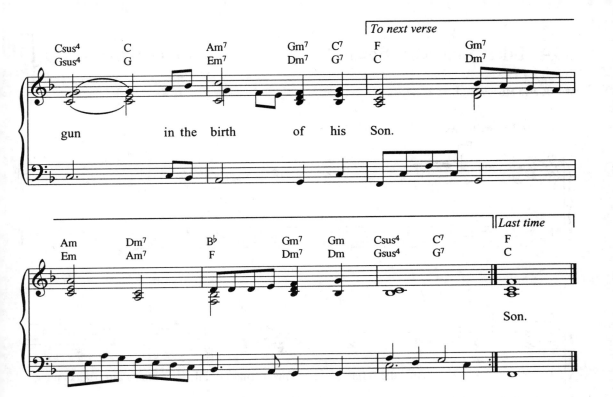

To next verse

gun   in the birth   of   his   Son.

Last time

Son.

2. Love came to dwell among us,
   love made flesh at Bethlehem,
   love from the beginning,
   our divine Creator's theme.

3. Life full of truth and beauty,
   life as it was meant to be,
   life from the beginning,
   and into eternity.

114 Like a candle flame

(The candle song)

Words and Music: Graham Kendrick

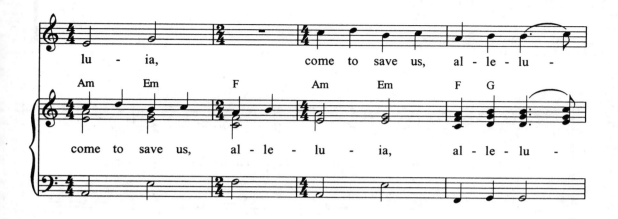

2. Stars and angels sing,
   yet the earth
   sleeps in shadows;
   can this tiny spark
   set a world on fire?

3. Yet his light shall shine
   from our lives,
   Spirit blazing,
   as we touch the flame
   of his holy fire.

115 Little donkey

Words and Music: Eric Boswell
arr. Andrew Moore

1. Lit-tle don - key, lit-tle don - key, on the dus - ty road,

got to keep on plod-ding on - wards with your pre - cious load.

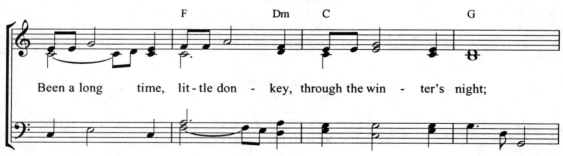

Been a long time, lit-tle don - key, through the win - ter's night;

don't give up now, lit-tle don - key, Beth-le-hem's in sight.

2. Little donkey, little donkey,
   on the dusty road,
   there are wise men, waiting for a
   sign to bring them here.
   Do not falter, little donkey,
   there's a star ahead;
   it will guide you, little donkey,
   to a cattle shed.

116 Little Jesus, sweetly sleep

Words: Traditional Czech carol
trans. Percy Dearmer

Music: Traditional Czech carol
collected by Martin Shaw
arr. Christopher Tambling

ROCKING 10 7 88 77

1. Lit-tle Je-sus, sweet-ly sleep, do not stir; we will lend a coat of fur; we will rock you, rock you, rock you, we will rock you, rock you, rock you; see the fur to keep you warm, snug-ly round your ti-ny form.

2. Mary's little baby, sleep, sweetly sleep,
sleep in comfort, slumber deep;
we will rock you, rock you, rock you,
we will rock you, rock you, rock you;
we will serve you all we can,
darling, darling little man.

117 Long ago and far away

Words and Music: Pamela Verrall
arr. David Peacock

CARIBBEAN CAROL

Calypso rhythm

1. Long a-go and far a-way in Beth-le-hem, a mo-ther lay her

new-born babe up-on the hay. He was the ho-ly

Je-sus-child, he was the ho-ly Je-sus. No-

well, no-well — let an-gels sing; no-

well, no-well — let church bells ring; no-

well, no-well, let ev - 'ry-thing sing

al - le-lu - ia to the ba-by boy! ba-by boy!

2. Shepherds on the mountain cold
   awoke when angel voices told,
   'Go and leave your lambs in fold –
   follow the star to Bethlehem;
   follow the star to Bethlehem!'

3. When they reached the open door
   and saw that love had gone before,
   they wond'ring knelt on dirty floor,
   worshipping baby Jesus there,
   worshipping baby Jesus.

118 Long ago, prophets knew

Words: Fred Pratt Green

Music: From *Piae Cantiones*
arr. Richard Lloyd

PERSONENT HODIE (THEODORIC) 666 66 and Refrain

1. Long a-go, pro-phets knew Christ would come, born a Jew,

come to make all things new, bear his peo-ple's bur-den,

Chorus

free-ly love and par-don. Ring, bells, ring, ring, ring!

Sing, choirs, sing, sing, sing! When he comes,

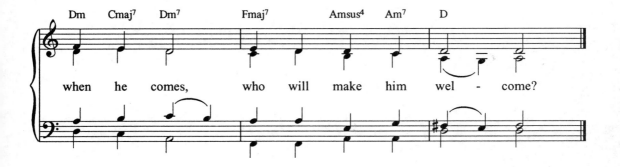

when he comes, who will make him wel - come?

2. God in time, God in man,
   this is God's timeless plan:
   he will come, as a man,
   born himself of woman,
   God divinely human.

3. Mary, hail! Though afraid,
   she believed, she obeyed.
   In her womb, God is laid:
   till the time expected,
   nurtured and protected.

4. Journey ends! Where afar
   Bethlem shines, like a star,
   stable door stands ajar.
   Unborn Son of Mary,
   Saviour, do not tarry!

119 Long ago there was born

Words: Unknown

Music: Adapted from Johannes Brahms
arr. Chris Mitchell

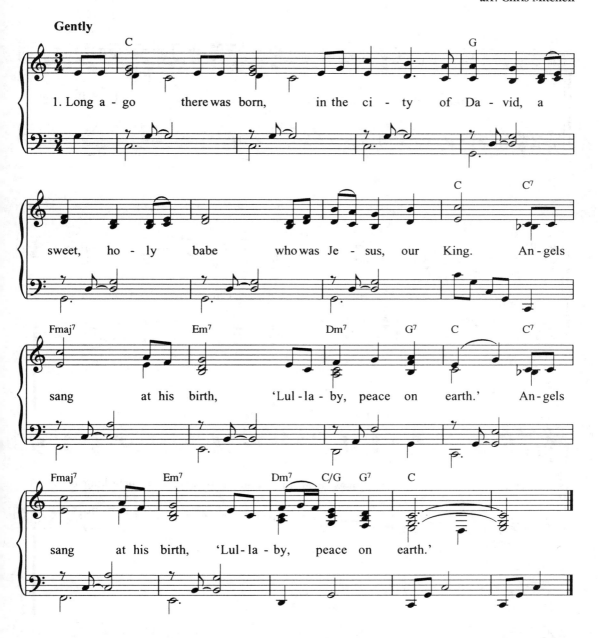

Gently

1. Long a - go there was born, in the ci - ty of Da - vid, a sweet, ho - ly babe who was Je - sus, our King. An - gels sang at his birth, 'Lul - la - by, peace on earth.' An - gels sang at his birth, 'Lul - la - by, peace on earth.'

2. Jesus came as a child from his Father in heaven,
and has shown us the way to be loving and kind.
While the stars sang above, 'Lullaby, God is love.'
While the stars sang above, 'Lullaby, God is love.'

120 Mary's boy child *(Long time ago in Bethlehem)*

Words and Music: Jester Hairston

2. While shepherds watched their flocks by night,
them see a bright new shining star.
Them hear a choir sing; the music
seemed to come from afar.

3. Now Joseph and his wife, Mary,
come to Bethlehem that night.
Them find no place to born the child.
Not a single room was in sight.

121 Look away to Bethlehem

Words and Music: Leslie Sturdy
arr. Chris Mitchell

Gently, not fast

1. Look   a - way   to   Beth - le -
2. Wan -   d'ring shep - herds saw   the
3. Let   the Christ - mas bells   ring

hem,   seek   the   star   up   in   the
star,   on   that night so   long a -
out   from   each stee - ple in   the

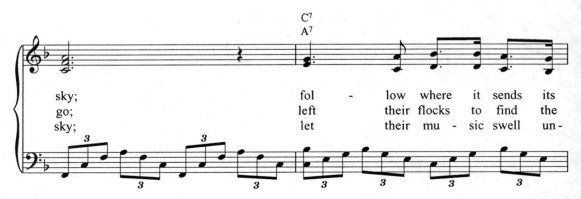

sky;   fol -   low where it   sends   its
go;   left   their flocks to   find   the
sky;   let   their mu - sic swell un -

122 Look to the skies

(Worship the King)

Words and Music: Graham Kendrick
arr. David Peacock

Triumphantly

1. Look to the skies, there's a ce-le-bra-tion; lift up your heads, join the an-gel-song, for our Cre-a-tor be-comes our Sa-viour, as a ba-by born! An-gels a-mazed bow in a-do-ra-tion: 'Glo-ry to God in the high-est heav'n!— Send the good news out to ev-'ry na-tion, for our hope has come.

Chorus

Worship the King — come, see his brightness; worship the King, his wonders tell: Jesus our King is born today — we welcome you, Emmanuel!

2. Wonderful counsellor, Mighty God, –
   Father for ever, the Prince of peace:
   there'll be no end to your rule of justice,
   for it shall increase.
   Light of your face, come to pierce our darkness;
   joy of your heart come to chase our gloom;
   star of the morning, a new day dawning,
   make our hearts your home.

3. Quietly he came as a helpless baby –
   one day in pow'r he will come again;
   swift through the skies he will burst with splendour
   on the earth to reign.
   Jesus, I bow at your manger lowly:
   now in my life let your will be done;
   live in my flesh by your Spirit holy
   till your kingdom comes.

123 Lord, make me thankful

Words and Music: James Wright
arr. Chris Mitchell

Lord, make me thank-ful and help me to see all the good things

gi-ven to me, for Christ-mas par-ties and the car-ols we sing,

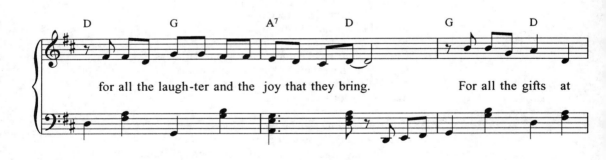

for all the laugh-ter and the joy that they bring. For all the gifts at

this time of year, that make our Christ-mas so full of cheer.

124 Lord, you left your throne

Words: Emily Elizabeth Steele Elliot

Music: Timothy Richard Matthews

MARGARET 10 8 11 8 and Refrain

1. Lord, you left your throne and your king - ly crown when you

came to this earth for me; but in Beth - le-hem's home there was

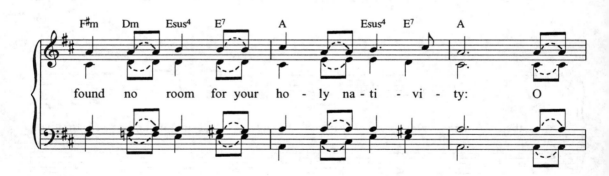

found no room for your ho - ly na - ti - vi - ty: O

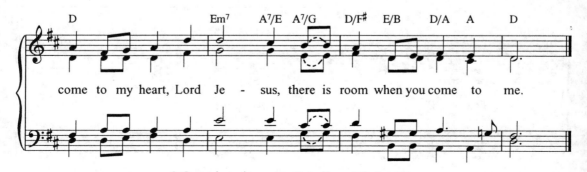

come to my heart, Lord Je - sus, there is room when you come to me.

2. Heaven's arches rang when the angels sang
   proclaiming your royal degree,
   but in lowly birth, Lord, you came to earth
   and in great humility:
   O come to my heart, Lord Jesus,
   there is room when you come to me.

3. The foxes found rest, and the birds their nest
   in the shade of the cedar tree;
   but no place was known you could call your own
   in the hillsides of Galilee.
   O come to my heart, Lord Jesus,
   there is room when you come to me.

4. When you came, O Lord, with the living word
   that should set your people free,
   then with mocking scorn and with crown of thorn
   they led you to Calvary:
   O come to my heart, Lord Jesus,
   your cross is my only plea.

5. When heav'n's arches ring and its choirs shall sing
   at your coming to victory,
   let your voice call me home, saying, 'Yes, there is room!'
   – there is room at your side for me!
   Then my heart shall rejoice, Lord Jesus,
   when you come and you call for me.

125 Love came down at Christmas

Words: Christina Georgina Rossetti

Music: Reginald Owen Morris

TUNE 1: HERMITAGE 67 67

1. Love came down at Christ - mas, Love all love - ly, Love di - vine;

Love was born at Christ - mas, star and an - gels gave the sign.

2. Worship we the Godhead,
   Love incarnate, Love divine;
   worship we our Jesus:
   but wherewith for sacred sign?

3. Love shall be our token,
   love be yours and love be mine,
   love to God and all men,
   love for plea and gift and sign.

Words: Christina Georgina Rossetti

Music: Malcolm Archer

TUNE 2: LOVE CAME DOWN 67 67

1. Love came down at Christ - mas, Love all love - ly, Love di - vine;

Love was born at Christ - mas, star and an - gels gave the sign.

Tune 1 © Copyright Oxford University Press, Great Clarendon Street,
Oxford OX2 6DP, UK. Used by permission.
Tune 2 © Copyright 1991 Kevin Mayhew Ltd.

126 Lully, lulla, thou little tiny child *(Coventry Carol)*

Words: Robert Croo, from the
Pageant of the Shearmen and Tailors

Music: Original tune of 1591
arr. Neil Jenkins

1. Lul-ly, lul-la, thou lit-tle ti-ny child, by by, lul-ly lul-lay. Thou lit-tle ti-ny child, lul-ly lul-la; by by, lul-ly lul-lay.

2. O sisters too, how may we do,
   for to preserve this day
   this poor youngling, for whom we sing,
   by by lully lullay?

3. Herod the king, in his raging,
   chargèd he hath this day
   his men of might, in his own sight,
   all young children to slay.

4. That woe is me, poor child for thee!
   and ever morn and day,
   for thy parting neither say nor sing,
   by by, lully lullay.

127 Mary had a baby

Words: West Indian Spiritual

Music: West Indian traditional melody
arr. Chris Mitchell

1. Ma - ry had a ba - by,
2. What did she name him?
3. Ma - ry named him Je - sus!

yes, Lord; Ma - ry had a ba - by, yes my Lord;
yes, Lord; what did she name him? yes, my Lord;
yes, Lord; Ma - ry named him Je - sus! yes, my Lord;

Ma - ry had a ba - by, yes, Lord; the
what did she name him? yes, Lord; the
Ma - ry named him Je - sus! yes, Lord; the

peo - ple keep a - com - ing for to see her child! see her child!

4. Where was he born?
   yes, Lord...

5. Born in a stable!
   yes, Lord...

6. Where did she lay him?
   yes, Lord...

7. Laid him in a manger!
   yes, Lord...

128 Mary had a little baby

Words and Music: Andy Silver
arr. Chris Mitchell

129 Mary, Joseph, manger and straw *(Jesus is born)*

Words and Music: Nick Harding
arr. Chris Mitchell

Lively/Bouncy!

1. Ma - ry, (Ma - ry), Jo - seph, (Jo - seph), man - ger and straw

look in (look in) won - der (won - der) at all they saw.

Chorus

Je - sus, Lord and Sa - viour, Je - sus is born.

Je - sus, Lord and Sa - viour, Je - sus is born.

2. Angels, (angels), singing (singing)
   high up above,
   saying (saying) Jesus (Jesus)
   brings joy and love.

3. Wise men (wise men) travel (travel),
   all night and day,
   with the (with the) star to (star to)
   show them the way.

4. Shepherds, (shepherds), angels (angels),
   wise men have gone,
   but we (but we) know that (know that)
   Jesus lives on.

130 Mary shivers

(Mary's child)

Words and Music: Philip Chapman and Stephanie Chapman
arr. Dave Bankhead

131 Meeknesss and majesty (This is your God)

Words and Music: Graham Kendrick

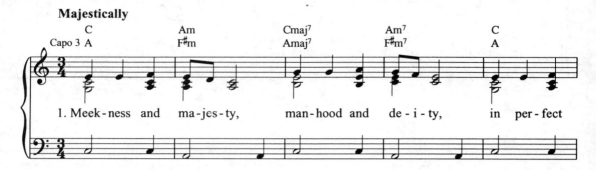

1. Meek-ness and ma-jes-ty, man-hood and de-i-ty, in per-fect

har-mo-ny, the Man who is God. Lord of e-ter-ni-ty

dwells in hu-ma-ni-ty, kneels in hu-mi-li-ty and wash-es our

feet. O what a mys-te-ry, meek-ness and ma-jes-ty,

2. Father's pure radiance,
   perfect in innocence,
   yet learns obedience
   to death on a cross.
   Suffering to give us life,
   conquering through sacrifice,
   and as they crucify
   prays: 'Father forgive.'

3. Wisdom unsearchable,
   God the invisible,
   love indestructible
   in frailty appears.
   Lord of infinity,
   stooping so tenderly,
   lifts our humanity
   to the heights of his throne.

132 My soul doth magnify the Lord

Words: From Luke 1

Music: Unknown
arr. Chris Mitchell

Gently

My soul doth mag-ni-fy the Lord, and my

spi-rit hath re-joiced in God my Sa-viour. For

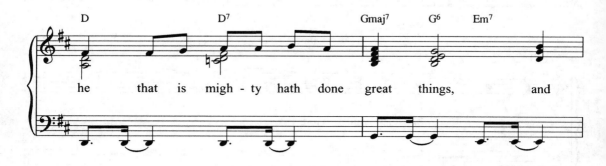

he that is migh-ty hath done great things, and

ho-ly is his name. My soul doth

133 No gift so wonderful

(Have we any room for Jesus?)

Words and Music: Susie Hare

Unhurried

1. No gift so won - der - ful, no love so beau - ti -
2. No gift so won - der - ful, no love so beau - ti -

ful, in just a hum - ble birth, hea-ven came down to earth.
ful; what are we meant to see — is it just his - to - ry?

And in the still of night,
And is he still, we find,

the world was gi - ven light, as in - to sin and
a ba - by in our mind, and is the sta - ble

shame, the love of hea - ven came.
scene all it will e - ver mean?

134 No room at the world

Words and Music: Graham Kendrick

1. I saw a pre-cious load on a lone-ly road when the sky was clear and cold, the don-key stum-bled, the young man held the reins. Well, the girl she looked down and her face was white, she knew her time was near;

2. Well, the innkeeper laughed and his eyes were cold,
   the girl began to cry;
   that's just another way of saying: 'please.'
   So he threw down some straw on the cattle floor
   and chased the hens away,
   turned and slammed the stable door behind,
   shook his head in the starlight.

3. Well, it was late and cold in the garden grove
   when the soldiers came in view,
   and Judas smiled as they took him from behind.
   And the priest said: 'kill,' and the crowd went wild
   on their bloody holiday.
   They whipped him and they stripped him
   and they left him there on the cross to die.

135 No room for the Saviour

Words and Music: Hilda M. Day

1. No room for the Saviour at Bethlehem's inn,
only a cattle shed; no room on this earth for the dear Son of God,
nowhere to lay his head.

2. O Lord in my heart there's a welcome for you:
gladly I now would say, 'Come in, precious Saviour; my heart and my life
both shall be yours today.

On - ly a cross did they give to my Lord,
Long have you wait - ed and long knocked in vain

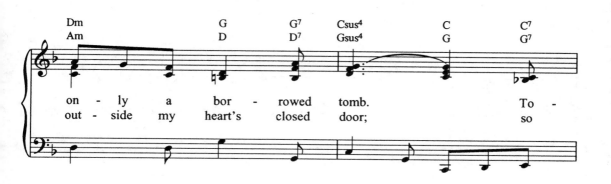

on - ly a bor - rowed tomb. To -
out - side my heart's closed door; so

day he is seek - ing a place in your heart — will you
cleanse me from sin, then, my Lord, en - ter in and

still say to him, 'No room'?
live there for e - ver - more!'

136 Now dawns the sun of righteousness
(Tell out, tell out the news)

Words and Music: Graham Kendrick

Joyful and bright

1. Now dawns the sun of right-eous-ness, and the dark-ness shall ne-ver his bright-ness dim; true light that lights the hearts of men, on-ly Son of the Fa-ther, Je-sus Christ.

Chorus

Tell out, tell out the news, on ev-'ry street pro-claim a Child is born, a Son is giv'n, and Je-sus is his name! Tell

out, tell out the news, our Sa-viour Christ has come, in

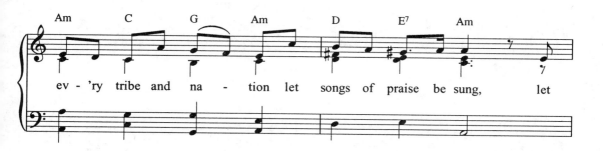

ev - 'ry tribe and na - tion let songs of praise be sung, let

songs of praise be sung!

2. Laughter and joy he will increase,
   all our burdens be lifted,
   oppression cease;
   the blood-stained battle-dress be burned,
   and the art of our warfare
   never more be learned.

3. So let us go, his witnesses,
   spreading news of his kingdom
   of righteousness,
   'til the whole world has heard the song,
   'til the harvest is gathered,
   then the end shall come.

137 O Christmas tree

Words: Ernst Anschütz
trans. Ruth Heller

Music: German melody
arr. Neil Jenkins

TANNENBAUM 87 87 88 87

1. O Christ-mas tree, O Christ-mas tree, O tree of green un - chang - ing. O

Christ-mas tree, O Christ-mas tree, O tree of green un - chang - ing. Your

boughs so green in sum-mer-time, do brave the snow of win-ter-time. O

Christ-mas tree, O Christ-mas tree, O tree of green un - chang - ing.

2. O Christmas tree, O Christmas tree,
   you set my heart a-singing.
   O Christmas tree, O Christmas tree,
   you set my heart a-singing.
   Like little stars, your candles bright,
   send to the world a wondrous light.
   O Christmas tree, O Christmas tree,
   you set my heart a-singing.

3. O Christmas tree, O Christmas tree,
   you come from God, eternal.
   O Christmas tree, O Christmas tree,
   you come from God, eternal.
   A symbol of the Lord of love,
   whom God to man sent from above.
   O Christmas tree, O Christmas tree,
   you come from God, eternal.

4. O Christmas tree, O Christmas tree,
   you speak of God, unchanging.
   O Christmas tree, O Christmas tree,
   you speak of God, unchanging.
   You tell us all to faithful be,
   and trust in God eternally.
   O Christmas tree, O Christmas tree,
   you speak of God, unchanging.

138 O come, all ye faithful

Words and Music: possibly by John Francis Wade
trans. Frederick Oakeley and others

ADESTE FIDELES Irregular and Refrain

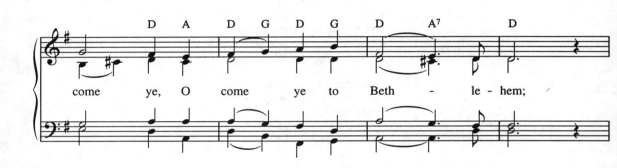

1. O come, all ye faith - ful, joy - ful and tri - um - phant, O
come ye, O come ye to Beth - le - hem;

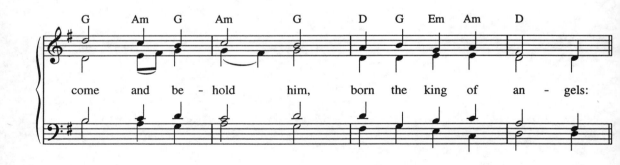

come and be - hold him, born the king of an - gels:

Chorus

O come
O come, let us a - dore him, O come, let us a - dore him, O

come, let us a - dore him, Christ the Lord.

2. God of God,
   Light of Light,
   lo, he abhors not the Virgin's womb;
   very God, begotten not created:

3. See how the shepherds,
   summoned to his cradle,
   leaving their flocks, draw nigh with lowly fear;
   we too will thither bend our joyful footsteps:

4. Lo, star-led chieftains,
   Magi, Christ adoring,
   offer him incense, gold and myrrh;
   we to the Christ-child bring our hearts' oblations:

5. Sing, choirs of angels,
   sing in exultation,
   sing, all ye citizens of heav'n above;
   glory to God in the highest:

6. Yea, Lord, we greet thee,
   born this happy morning,
   Jesu, to thee be glory giv'n;
   Word of the Father, now in flesh appearing:

139 O come and join the dance

Words and Music: Graham Kendrick

(verse 3 instrumental)

1. O come and join the dance that all be-gan so long a-go, when
Christ the Lord was born in Beth-le-hem. Through
all the years of dark-ness still the dance goes on and on,
take my hand and come and join the song.

shed your hea-vy load and dance your wor-ries all a-way, for
He came to break the pow'r of sin and turn your night to day, O,

laugh-ter ring and an-gels sing and joy be all a-round, for
And if you seek with all your heart he sure-ly can be found,

Chorus

Men Re-

140 O come, O come Emmanuel

Words: From the *Great O Antiphons*
trans. John Mason Neale

Music: Adapted by Thomas Helmore
from a French Missal
arr. Colin Hand

VENI EMMANUEL LM and Refrain

1. O come, O come, Emmanuel, and ransom captive Israel, that mourns in lonely exile here, until the Son of God appear. Rejoice, rejoice! Emmanuel shall come to thee, O Israel.

2. O come, thou rod of Jesse, free
   thine own from Satan's tyranny;
   from depths of hell thy people save,
   and give them vict'ry o'er the grave.

3. O come, thou dayspring, come and cheer
   our spirits by thine advent here;
   disperse the gloomy clouds of night,
   and death's dark shadows put to flight.

4. O come, thou key of David, come
   and open wide our heav'nly home;
   make safe the way that leads on high,
   and close the path to misery.

5. O come, O come, thou Lord of might,
   who to thy tribes on Sinai's height
   in ancient times didst give the Law,
   in cloud and majesty and awe.

141 Of the Father's heart begotten

Words: *Corde natus ex parentis* by
Aurelius Clemens Prudentius
trans. John Mason Neale
and Henry William Baker

Music: Plainsong melody
from *Piae Cantiones*
arr. Chris Mitchell

CORDE NATUS (DIVINUM MYSTERIUM) 87 87 87 7

1. Of the Fa-ther's heart be-got-ten

when no world had come to be, he is

Al-pha and O-me-ga, he the source the

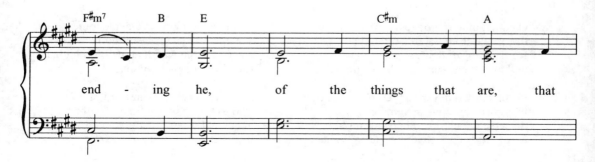

end-ing he, of the things that are, that

have ... been, and that fu - ture years shall

see: e - ver - more and e - ver - more.

2. By his word was all created;
   he commanded; it was done;
   earth and sky and boundless ocean
   in their threefold order one;
   all that sees the moon's soft radiance,
   all that breathes beneath the sun:
   evermore and evermore.

3. Happy is that day for ever
   when the virgin, filled with grace,
   by the Spirit's pow'r conceiving
   bore the Saviour of our race;
   and the babe, the world's Redeemer
   first revealed his sacred face:
   evermore and evermore.

4. This is he whom priests and poets
   sang of old with one accord;
   whom the voices of the prophets
   promised in their faithful word:
   now he shines, the long-expected;
   let creation praise its Lord:
   evermore and evermore.

5. Praise him, all you hosts of heaven;
   praise him, angels in the height;
   pow'rs, dominions, bow before him,
   and extol his glorious might;
   let no tongue on earth be silent,
   let each heart and voice unite:
   evermore and evermore.

142 Oh, come, little children

Words and Music: Johann A. P. Schulz

SCHULZ 65 65 D

1. Oh, come, lit-tle child-ren, oh, come, one and all, to Beth-le-hem's sta-ble, in Beth-le-hem's stall, and see with re-joic-ing this glo-ri-ous sight, our Fa-ther in hea-ven has sent us this night.

2. Oh, see in the manger in hallowèd light,
a star throws its beam on this holiest sight.
In clean swaddling clothes lies the heavenly child,
more lovely than angels, this baby so mild.

3. Oh, there lies the Christ Child, on hay and on straw;
the shepherds are kneeling before him with awe.
And Mary and Joseph smile on him with love,
while angels are singing sweet songs from above.

143 Oh town of Bethlehem

Words and Music: James Wright
arr. Chris Mitchell

1. Oh town of Beth-le-hem be-neath the stars of heav'n, what is the sec-ret you hold this night? God's own be-got-ten Son, hea-ven's a-noint-ed one has come down. down. Come now and be-hold the new-born King, glo-ry of Is-ra-el,

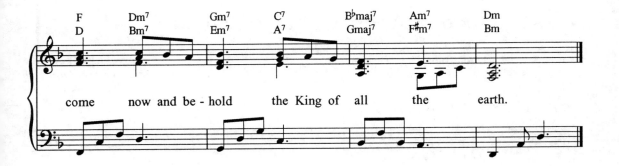

come   now and be - hold   the King of   all   the   earth.

2. Oh what a glorious plan
   that brought your love to man;
   born in a stable so cold and bare.
   From heaven's majesty
   to earth's humanity
   love came down.

144 O little one sweet, O little one mild

Words: Samuel Scheidt, trans. Percy Dearmer, alt.

Music: Melody from
Samuel Scheidt's *Tabulaturbuch*
harm. Martin Shaw

O JESULEIN SÜSS 10 9 88 10

1. O lit - tle one sweet, O lit - tle one mild, thy Fa - ther's
pur - pose thou hast ful - filled; thou cam'st from heav'n to
dwell be - low, to share the joys and tears we
know, O lit - tle one sweet, O lit - tle one mild.

2. O little one sweet, O little one mild,
   with joy thou hast the whole world filled;
   thou camest here from heav'n's domain,
   to bring us comfort in our pain,
   O little one sweet, O little one mild.

3. O little one sweet, O little one mild,
   in thee Love's beauties are all distilled;
   then light in us thy love's bright flame,
   that we may give thee back the same,
   O little one sweet, O little one mild.

Words: Samuel Scheidt, trans. Percy Dearmer, alt.

Music: Melody from
Samuel Scheidt's *Tabulaturbuch*
harm. Johann Sebastian Bach

Another harmonisation

1. O lit - tle one sweet, O lit - tle one mild, thy Fa - ther's pur - pose thou hast ful - filled; thou cam'st from heav'n to dwell be - low, to share the joys and tears we know, O lit - tle one sweet, O lit - tle one mild.

145 O little town of Bethlehem

Words: Phillips Brooks, alt.

Music: Traditional English melody
collected and adapted by Ralph Vaughan Williams

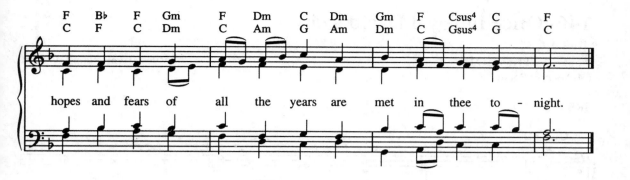

hopes and fears of all the years are met in thee to - night.

2. O morning stars, together
proclaim the holy birth,
and praises sing to God the King,
and peace upon the earth.
For Christ is born of Mary;
and, gathered all above,
while mortals sleep, the angels keep
their watch of wond'ring love.

3. How silently, how silently,
the wondrous gift is giv'n!
So God imparts to human hearts
the blessings of his heav'n.
No ear may hear his coming;
but in this world of sin,
where meek souls will receive him, still
the dear Christ enters in.

4. O holy child of Bethlehem,
descend to us, we pray;
cast out our sin, and enter in,
be born in us today.
We hear the Christmas angels
the great glad tidings tell:
O come to us, abide with us,
our Lord Emmanuel.

146 Once in royal David's city

Words: Cecil Frances Alexander;
v.4: Michael Forster

Music: Henry John Gauntlett

IRBY 87 87 77

2. He came down to earth from heaven,
   who is God and Lord of all,
   and his shelter was a stable,
   and his cradle was a stall;
   with the poor and meek and lowly,
   lived on earth our Saviour holy.

3. And through all his wondrous childhood
   day by day like us he grew;
   he was little, weak and helpless,
   tears and smiles like us he knew;
   and he feeleth for our sadness,
   and he shareth in our gladness.

4. Still among the poor and lowly
   hope in Christ is brought to birth,
   with the promise of salvation
   for the nations of the earth;
   still in him our life is found
   and our hope of heav'n is crowned.

5. And our eyes at last shall see him
   through his own redeeming love,
   for that child so dear and gentle
   is our Lord in heav'n above;
   and he leads his children on
   to the place where he is gone.

6. Not in that poor lowly stable,
   with the oxen standing by,
   we shall see him, but in heaven,
   set at God's right hand on high;
   when like stars his children crowned,
   all in white shall wait around.

147 Once upon a universe

Words and Music: Graham Kendrick
arr. Jonathan Savage

148 On Christmas night all Christians sing

Words: Traditional English carol, alt.

Music: Traditional English melody collected and arr. Ralph Vaughan Williams

SUSSEX CAROL 88 88 88

1. On Christ-mas night all Christ-ians sing, to hear the news the an-gels bring, on Christ-mas night all Christ-ians sing, to hear the news the an-gels bring, news of great joy, news of great mirth, news of our mer-ci-ful King's birth.

2. Then why should we on earth be so sad,
   since our Redeemer made us glad,
   then why should we on earth be so sad,
   since our Redeemer made us glad,
   when from our sin he set us free,
   all for to gain our liberty?

3. When sin departs before his grace,
   then life and health come in its place,
   when sin departs before his grace,
   then life and health come in its place,
   angels and earth with joy may sing,
   all for to see the new-born King.

4. All out of darkness we have light,
   which made the angels sing this night:
   all out of darkness we have light,
   which made the angels sing this night:
   'Glory to God and peace to men,
   now and for evermore. Amen.'

149 Over the world this Christmas morn

Words and Music: Joan Robinson
arr. Chris Mitchell

2. Over the world and over the sea
   the message rings out that Jesus loves me,
   that Jesus loves me, that Jesus loves me,
   the message rings out that Jesus loves me.

3. Over the world, I know it is true,
   the message rings out that Jesus loves you,
   that Jesus loves you, that Jesus loves you,
   the message rings out that Jesus loves you.

4. Over the world, let your voices sing,
   the message rings out that Jesus is King,
   that Jesus is King, that Jesus is King,
   the message rings out that Jesus is King.

150 O what a gift!

Words and Music: Pat Uhl Howard
arr. Betty Pulkingham

Joyfully, with a driving rhythm

O what a gift! what a won-der-ful gift! Who can tell the won-ders of the Lord? Let us o-pen our eyes, our ears, and our hearts; it is Christ the Lord, it is he!

1. In the still-ness of the night when the world was a-sleep, the al-
2. On the night be-fore he died it was Pass-o-ver night, and he
3. On the hill of Cal-va-ry the world held its breath; for
4. Ear-ly on that morn-ing when the world was sleep-ing,
5. Some day with the saints we will come be-fore our Fa-ther, and

151 O what a mystery I see

Words and Music: Graham Kendrick
arr. Christopher Norton

Brightly

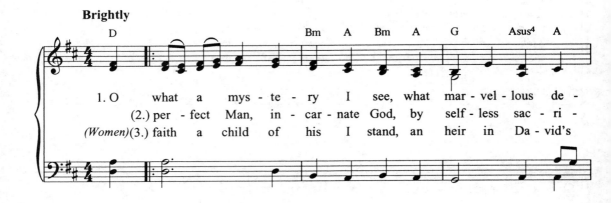

1. O what a mys-te-ry I see, what mar-vel-lous de-
(2.) per-fect Man, in-car-nate God, by self-less sac-ri-
(Women)(3.) faith a child of his I stand, an heir in Da-vid's

sign, that God should come as one of us, a
fice des-troyed our sin-ful his-to-ry, all
line, roy-al de-scend-ant by his blood des-

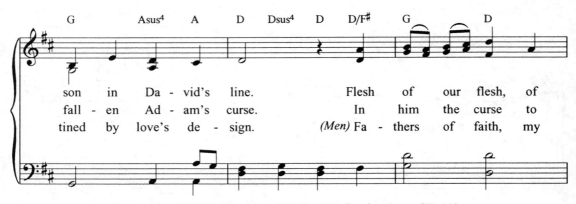

son in Da-vid's line. Flesh of our flesh, of
fall-en Ad-am's curse. In him the curse to
tined by love's de-sign. (Men) Fa-thers of faith, my

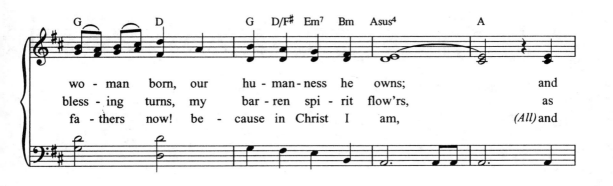

wo - man born, our hu - man - ness he owns; and
bless - ing turns, my bar - ren spi - rit flow'rs, as
fa - thers now! be - cause in Christ I am, *(All)* and

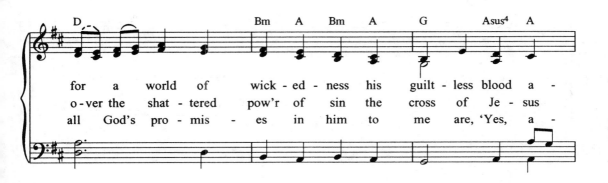

for a world of wick - ed - ness his guilt - less blood a -
o - ver the shat - tered pow'r of sin the cross of Je - sus
all God's pro - mis - es in him to me are, 'Yes, a -

1st and 2nd times

tones. 2. This
tow'rs. *(Women)* 3. By

3rd time

- men'! 4. No more then as a child of earth must

I my life-time spend — his his-to-ry, his des-ti-ny are

mine to ap-pre-hend. O what a Sa-viour, what a Lord, O

Mas-ter, bro-ther, friend! What mi-ra-cle has

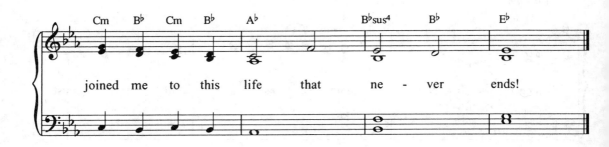

joined me to this life that ne - ver ends!

152 O worship the Lord in the beauty of holiness

Words: John Samuel Bewley Monsell

Music: Melody from the Rheinhardt MS, Üttingen

WAS LEBET 13 10 13 10

1. O wor - ship the Lord in the beau - ty of ho - li - ness; bow down be - fore him, his glo - ry pro - claim; with gold of o - be - dience, and in - cense of low - li - ness, kneel and a - dore him: the Lord is his name.

2. Low at his feet lay thy burden of carefulness:
   high on his heart he will bear it for thee,
   comfort thy sorrows, and answer thy prayerfulness,
   guiding thy steps as may best for thee be.

3. Fear not to enter his courts in the slenderness
   of the poor wealth thou wouldst reckon as thine:
   truth in its beauty, and love in its tenderness,
   these are the off'rings to lay on his shrine.

4. These, though we bring them in trembling and fearfulness,
   he will accept for the name that is dear;
   mornings of joy give for evenings of tearfulness,
   trust for our trembling and hope for our fear.

5. O worship the Lord in the beauty of holiness;
   bow down before him, his glory proclaim;
   with gold of obedience, and incense of lowliness,
   kneel and adore him: the Lord is his name.

153 Past three o'clock

Words: George Ratcliffe Woodward

Music: Traditional English melody
arr. Charles Wood

PAST THREE A'CLOCK 55 55 and Refrain

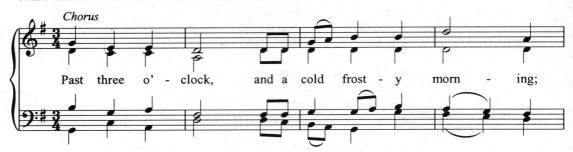

Chorus

Past three o'-clock, and a cold frost-y morn - ing;

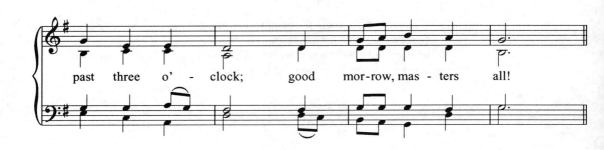

past three o'-clock; good mor-row, mas-ters all!

1. Born is a ba - by, gen-tle as may be,

son of th'e - ter - nal Fa-ther su - per-nal.

Chorus

Past three o' - clock, and a cold frost - y morn - ing;

After last verse Fine

past three o' - clock; good mor-row, mas - ters all!

2. Seraph choir singeth,
   angel bell ringeth:
   hark how they rhyme it,
   time it and chime it.

3. Mid earth rejoices
   hearing such voices
   ne'ertofore so well
   carolling 'Nowell'.

4. Hinds o'er the pearly
   dewy lawn early
   seek the high stranger
   laid in the manger.

5. Light out of star-land
   leadeth from far land
   princes, to meet him,
   worship and greet him.

6. Myrrh from full coffer,
   incense they offer:
   nor is the golden
   treasure withholden.

7. Thus they: I pray you,
   up, sirs, nor stay you
   till ye confess him
   likewise, and bless him.

154 Peace to you

Words and Music: Graham Kendrick

155 People awaken, open your eyes

(Light of the world)

Words and Music: Trevor Burch
arr. Susie Hare

1. Peo-ple a - wak - en, o-pen your eyes, see how the
an - gels ride through the skies; dark-ness has end -
ed, a new day has dawned, pro-mised Mes - si - ah is
born, God's on-ly Son. Light of the world, light from a -

2. Child of the Father, bringer of peace
   to ev'ry soul that longs for release,
   bring us the liberty won on the tree,
   taking our sin, making us whole, setting us free.

3. The zeal of the Father has done great things –
   Jesus is risen with healing wings!
   Daystar eternal, rule from your throne,
   loving your people and leading them on.

156 Riding high and low

(Riding high)

Words and Music: Roger Jones
arr. Donald Thomson

1. Rid-ing high and low, look-ing for a king, rid-ing o-ver de-serts, with the gifts we bring.

Chorus
Frank-in-cense and myrrh, gold we bring to him, these are what we'll give and our hearts to him.

2. Over mountains high,
over deserts dry,
on to find this baby,
looking in the sky!

3. On we go to Herod,
but he'll turn so green,
when we tell of Jesus,
and the star we've seen.

4. We are nearly there,
might get there today;
star is still above us
showing us the way.

157 Ring out the bells

Words: Michael Perry

Music: Traditional English melody
arr. Chris Mitchell

PAST THREE A'CLOCK 55 55 and Refrain

Chorus

Ring out the bells, the joy-ful news is break-ing. Ring out the bells, for Je-sus Christ is born.

after last verse Fine

1. An - gels in won - der sing of his glo - ry.

Shep - herds re - tur - ning tell us the sto - ry.

2. Let all creation
worship before him;
earth bring him homage,
heaven adore him.

3. Prophets have spoken,
hark to their warning:
shadows are passing,
soon comes the morning.

158 Rumours of angels

Words and Music: Graham Kendrick

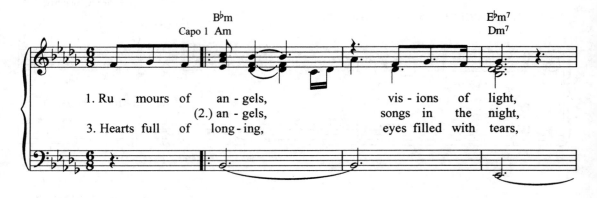

1. Ru - mours of an - gels, vis - ions of light,
(2.) an - gels, songs in the night,
3. Hearts full of long - ing, eyes filled with tears,

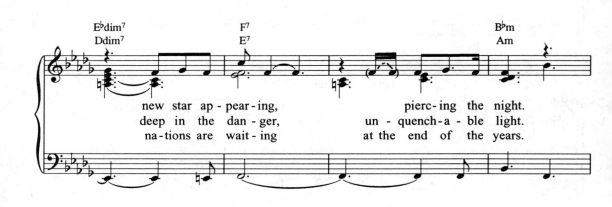

new star ap - pear - ing, pierc - ing the night.
deep in the dan - ger, un - quench - a - ble light.
na - tions are wait - ing at the end of the years.

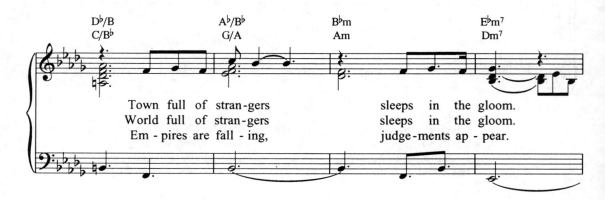

Town full of stran - gers sleeps in the gloom.
World full of stran - gers sleeps in the gloom.
Em - pires are fall - ing, judge - ments ap - pear.

159 See, amid the winter's snow

Words: Edward Caswall

Music: John Goss

HUMILITY (OXFORD) 77 77 and Refrain

1. See, a-mid the win-ter's snow, born for us on earth be-low,

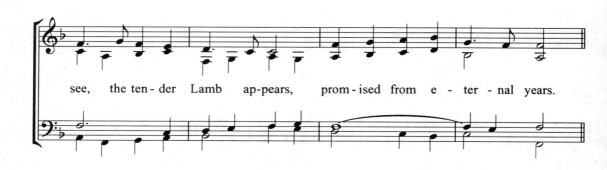

see, the ten-der Lamb ap-pears, prom-ised from e-ter-nal years.

Hail, thou e-ver-bles-sed morn, hail, re-demp-tion's hap-py dawn!

Sing through all Je-ru-sa-lem, Christ is born in Beth-le-hem.

2. Lo, within a manger lies
   he who built the starry skies;
   he who, throned in height sublime,
   sits amid the cherubim.

3. Say, you holy shepherds, say,
   what your joyful news today?
   Wherefore have you left your sheep
   on the lonely mountain steep?

4. 'As we watched at dead of night,
   there appeared a wondrous light;
   angels, singing peace on earth,
   told us of the Saviour's birth.'

5. Sacred infant, all divine,
   what a tender love was thine,
   thus to come from highest bliss,
   down to such a world as this!

6. Virgin mother, Mary, blest,
   by the joys that fill thy breast,
   pray for us, that we may prove
   worthy of the Saviour's love.

160 See him lying on a bed of straw

Words and Music: Michael Perry
arr. Christopher Tambling

CALYPSO CAROL Irregular and Refrain

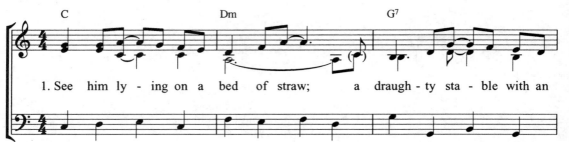

1. See him ly - ing on a bed of straw; a draugh - ty sta - ble with an

o - pen door.   Ma - ry cra - dl - ing the babe she bore: the

Prince of Glo - ry is his name.   O

Beth - le - hem   to see the Lord   of love a - gain:

2. Star of silver, sweep across the skies,
   show where Jesus in the manger lies;
   shepherds, swiftly from your stupor rise
   to see the Saviour of the world!

3. Angels, sing again the song you sang,
   sing the glory of God's gracious plan;
   sing that Bethlehem's little baby can
   be the Saviour of us all.

4. Mine are riches, from your poverty;
   from your innocence, eternity;
   mine, forgiveness by your death for me,
   child of sorrow for my joy.

161 See, to us a child is born

Words: Timothy Dudley-Smith

Music: *The Parish Choir*
arr. Chris Mitchell

INNOCENTS 77 77

Joyfully

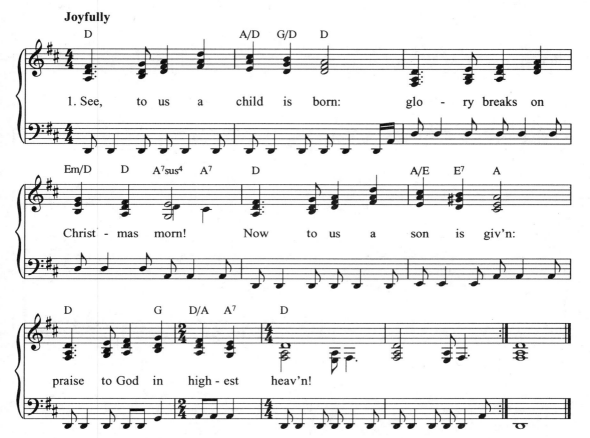

1. See, to us a child is born: glo-ry breaks on Christ-mas morn! Now to us a son is giv'n: praise to God in high-est heav'n!

2. On his shoulder rule shall rest:
   in him all the earth be blest!
   Wise and wonderful his name:
   heaven's Lord in human frame!

3. Mighty God, who mercy brings:
   Lord of lords and King of kings!
   Father of eternal days:
   ev'ry creature sing his praise!

4. Everlasting Prince of peace:
   truth and righteousness increase!
   He shall reign from shore to shore:
   Christ is King for evermore!

162 Shepherds found him

(We have found him)

Words and Music: Mark and Helen Johnson
arr. Chris Mitchell

let all the an - gels sing.

Such an a - maz - ing thing,

let all the an - gels sing.

2. Wise men found him,
   led by the star, came from afar,
   now they kneel in worship,
   bringing their gifts to him.

3. We have found him,
   here in this place, our journey ends,
   for we have found him,
   Jesus the King is here.

163 Silently we watch

Words and Music: Linda Mawson

Fairly fast and flowing

HAZELMERE

1. Si - lent - ly we watch as our God steps down from his glo - rious throne in - to this poor world. Ta - king to him - self his ti - ny hu - man form, he who made the world lies in Ma - ry's arms. We wor-ship you, Im - man - u - el, we a -

2. Thankfully we take from your gracious hand
   gifts of priceless worth,
   bought with your own blood.
   Lifted up and reconciled to God again,
   all our sins forgiven,
   sons of God we stand.

3. Joyfully we wait till our Lord shall come,
   robed in majesty
   for all the world to see.
   Glorious in power, he will judge the world.
   Righteous King of kings,
   he will reign for ever.

164 Silent night

Words: Joseph Mohr trans. John Freeman Young

Music: Franz Grüber
arr. Colin Hand

STILLE NACHT Irregular

1. Silent night, holy night. All is calm, all is bright, round yon virgin mother and child; holy infant, so tender and mild, sleep in heavenly peace, sleep in heavenly peace.

2. Silent night, holy night.
   Shepherds quake at the sight,
   glories stream from heaven afar,
   heav'nly hosts sing alleluia:
   Christ the Saviour is born,
   Christ the Saviour is born.

3. Silent night, holy night.
   Son of God, love's pure light,
   radiant beams from thy holy face,
   with the dawn of redeeming grace:
   Jesus, Lord, at thy birth,
   Jesus, Lord, at thy birth.

165 Since the day the angel came *(Thorns in the straw)*

Words and Music: Graham Kendrick

1. Since the day the an - gel came it seemed that
(2.) blan - ket on the floor of a
(3.) words of an - cient seers tum - bled
(4.) watched him through the years, her joy was
(5.) gainst a dark - 'ning sky, the one she

e - v'ry-thing had changed. The on - ly cer-tain thing was the
va - cant cat - tle-stall, but there the child was born. She
down the cen - tu - ries — a vir-gin shall con-ceive God
min - gled with her tears, and she'd feel it all a - gain, the
loved was lift - ed high, and with his dy - ing breath she heard him

child that moved with-in on the road that would not end, wind - ing
held him in her arms and as she laid him down to sleep, she won-dered,
with us, Prince of Peace. Man of sor-rows – stran-gest name. Oh Jo - seph,
glo - ry and the shame. And when the mi - ra - cles be - gan, she won-dered,
say, 'Fa-ther, for-give!' and to the cri - mi - nal be - side, 'To-day with

166 Sing, all the earth

Words and Music: Graham Kendrick

167 Sing and celebrate

Words and Music: Greg Leavers
arr. Chris Mitchell

Sing and ce - le - brate (sing and ce - le - brate); God gave Je - sus
(God gave Je - sus); Light for all the world (Light for all the world);
born at Christ - mas (born at Christ - mas time).

1. Je - sus, our light,
2. God so loved us,

shines bright, what de-light; came to
gave us Je-sus; Lord, we

reach us, teach us, lead us;
thank you, love you, serve you;

CODA

Je - sus, Light of the world,

God's great gift of love.

168 Sing lullaby!

Words: Sabine Baring-Gould

Music: Old Basque Noël
arr. Philip Moore

THE INFANT KING 494 89 94

1. Sing lul - la - by! Lul - la - by ba - by, now re - clin - ing, sing lul - la -
by! Hush, do not wake the in - fant king. An - gels are watch - ing, stars are
shi - ning o - ver the place where he is ly - ing: sing lul - la - by!

2. Sing lullaby!
   Lullaby baby, now a-sleeping,
   sing lullaby!
   Hush, do not wake the infant king.
   Soon will come sorrow with the morning,
   soon will come bitter grief and weeping:
   sing lullaby!

3. Sing lullaby!
   Lullaby baby, now a-dozing,
   sing lullaby!
   Hush, do not wake the infant king.
   Soon comes the cross, the nails, the piercing,
   then in the grave at last reposing:
   sing lullaby!

4. Sing lullaby!
   Lullaby! is the baby awaking?
   Sing lullaby.
   Hush, do not stir the infant king.
   Dreaming of Easter, gladsome morning,
   conquering death, its bondage breaking:
   sing lullaby!

169 Sleep, holy child

Words and Music: James Wright
arr. Chris Mitchell

2. Two thousand years have passed and gone
   yet we remember the night your glory shone.
   Nations may rise, kingdoms may fall,
   yet the light of heaven shines on
   Jesus, the Saviour of all.

170 So many centuries *(Nothing will ever be the same)*

Words and Music: Graham Kendrick

1. So many centuries of watching and waiting,
but when the moment came, well nobody saw,
traders and travellers hurried by,
and life went on just like before.

2. In all the clamour just a new baby crying,
one more poor family shut out in the cold.
Nothing unusual, sad to say,
hasn't it always been this way?

3. So rare we recognise our history in the making,
meet angels unawares and pass on our way,
blind to the moment of destiny,
while precious years just slip away, slip away.

4. And now a door is standing open before you,
casting its light into the darkness around,
stop for a moment, step inside,
tonight could be your Bethlehem.

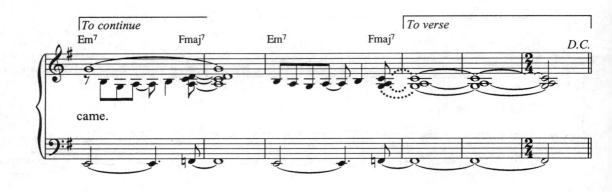

child   is   born,   a   Son   is   giv'n,

and his King - dom   of   peace   will

ne - ver end,   ne - ver end,   no!

And

171 Thank you, Jesus

Words and Music: Capt. Alan J. Price CA
arr. Chris Mitchell

Thank you, Je - sus, thank you, Lord for giv - ing up your glo - ry, to be - come a ba - by in Beth - le - hem, as we hear in the Christ - mas sto - ry. sto - ry. You did not stay a ti - ny child, you grew up big and strong; to help us know and choose what's right, and

1st time
2nd time

172 The angel Gabriel from heaven came

Words: Sabine Baring-Gould

Music: Traditional Basque melody
arr Richard Lloyd

BIRJINA GAZTETTOBAT ZEGOEN 10 10 12 10

1. The an-gel Ga-bri-el from hea-ven came, his wings as drift-ed snow, his eyes as flame. 'All hail,' said he,'thou low-ly maid-en Ma - ry, most high-ly fa-voured la - dy.' Glo - ri - a!

2. For known a blessèd Mother thou shalt be.
   All generations laud and honour thee.
   Thy Son shall be Emmanuel, by seers foretold,
   most highly favoured lady.' Gloria!

3. Then gentle Mary meekly bowed her head.
   'To me be as it pleaseth God,' she said.
   'My soul shall laud and magnify his holy name.'
   Most highly favoured lady! Gloria!

4. Of her, Emmanuel, the Christ, was born
   in Bethlehem, all on a Christmas morn;
   and Christian folk throughout the world will ever say:
   'Most highly favoured lady.' Gloria!

173 The first Nowell

Words: from William Sandys'
Christmas Carols, Ancient and Modern, alt.

Music: Traditional English melody
arr. John Stainer

THE FIRST NOWELL Irregular and Refrain

1. The first No - well the an - gel did say was to cer - tain poor

shep - herds in fields as they lay: in fields where they lay

keep - ing their sheep, on a cold win - ter's night that was so deep.

Chorus

No - well, No - well, No - well, No - well,

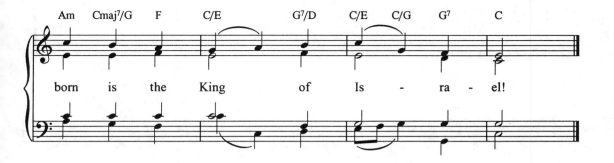

born is the King of Is - ra - el!

2. They lookèd up and saw a star,
shining in the east, beyond them far,
and to the earth it gave great light,
and so it continued both day and night.

3. And by the light of that same star,
three wise men came from country far;
to seek for a king was their intent,
and to follow the star wherever it went.

4. This star drew nigh to the north-west,
o'er Bethlehem it took its rest,
and there it did both stop and stay
right over the place where Jesus lay.

5. Then entered in those wise men three,
full rev'rently upon their knee,
and offered there in his presence,
their gold and myrrh and frankincense.

6. Then let us all with one accord
sing praises to our heav'nly Lord,
who with the Father we adore
and Spirit blest for evermore.

174 The God we seek

Words: Bryn Austin Rees

Music: Tom Cunningham

JESUS IS BORN

1. The God we seek, be-yond all thought, has
now his Christ-mas won-der wrought: be-hold, the seek-er is the sought!
Wait-ing end-ed, man be-friend-ed: Je-sus is born!

2. Love is the manger where he lies,
   love is the cross on which he dies;
   stronger than death shall love arise!
   Glorious meekness, pow'r in weakness:
   Jesus is born!

3. Into the love of Christ the King
   our lives, our world, in faith we bring:
   the sin, the pain, the suffering.
   God esteems us, Christ redeems us:
   Jesus is born!

175 The holly and the ivy

Words: Emily Chisholm

Music: English folk carol
arr. Adrian Vernon Fish

THE HOLLY AND THE IVY 76 87 (Irregular)

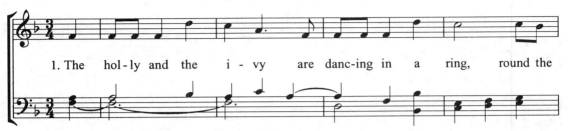

1. The hol-ly and the i-vy are danc-ing in a ring, round the

ber-ry-bright red can-dles and the white and shin-ing King.

2. Oh, one is for God's people
   in ev'ry age and day.
   We are watching for his coming.
   We believe and we obey.

3. And two is for the prophets
   and for the light they bring.
   They are candles in the darkness,
   all alight for Christ the King.

4. And three for John the Baptist.
   He calls on us to sing:
   'O prepare the way for Jesus Christ,
   he is coming, Christ the King.'

5. And four for mother Mary.
   'I cannot see the way,
   but you promise me a baby.
   I believe you. I obey.'

6. And Christ is in the centre,
   for this is his birthday,
   with the shining lights of Christmas
   singing: 'He has come today!'

176 The light of Christ

Words and Music: Donald Fishel
arr. Betty Pulkingham

The light of Christ has come in-to the world; the light of Christ has to the world; the light of Christ

177 The promised time arrives

Words: Martin E. Leckebusch

Music: Johann Crüger
arr. Chris Mitchell

NUN DANKET 67 67 66 66

Rhythmically (♩ = 120)

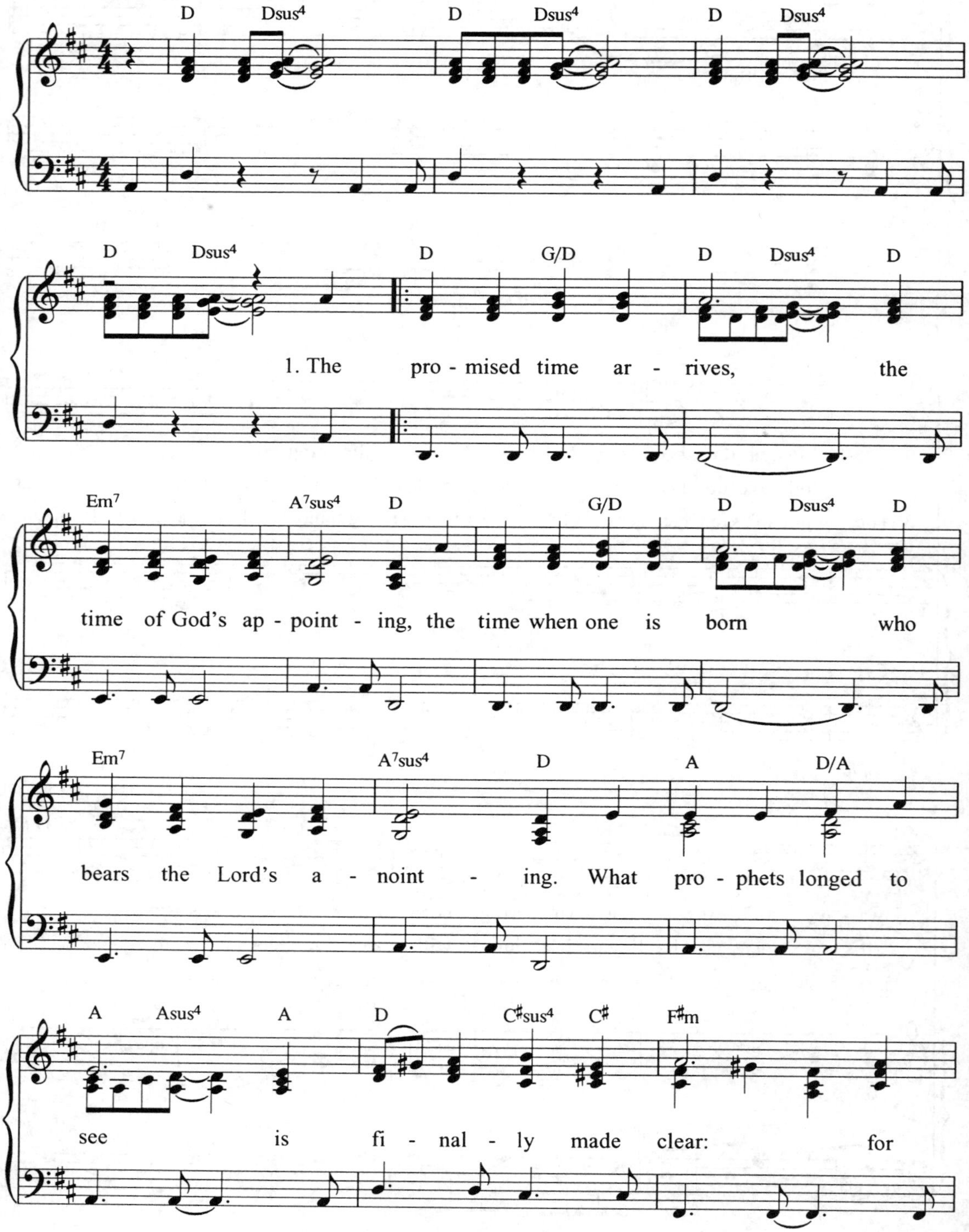
D Dsus4 D Dsus4 D Dsus4
D Dsus4 D G/D D Dsus4 D
1. The pro - mised time ar - rives, the
Em7 A7sus4 D G/D D Dsus4 D
time of God's ap - point - ing, the time when one is born who
Em7 A7sus4 D A D/A
bears the Lord's a - noint - ing. What pro - phets longed to
A Asus4 A D C#sus4 C# F#m
see is fi - nal - ly made clear: for

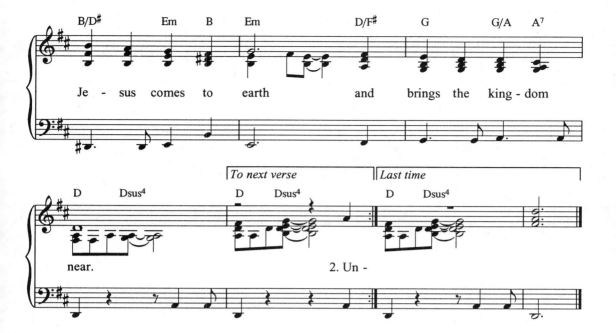

Je - sus comes to earth and brings the king - dom near.

To next verse

Last time

2. Un -

2. Unnumbered angels sing
   in joyful acclamation,
   for Christ the Lord is born,
   the bringer of salvation;
   there in a manger lies
   the Lord of heav'n and earth,
   who dignifies our life
   by sharing human birth.

3. He comes as David's heir
   and Abraham's descendant,
   yet takes no worldly throne
   with royal gold resplendent;
   though rulers seek him out
   to worship or to slay,
   no pow'r devised on earth
   can take his crown away.

4. The way to God he shows
   to all who will receive him –
   what light and life are ours
   if we will but believe him!
   The Son of God is here,
   so full of truth and grace;
   God's glory is disclosed
   upon a human face.

178 The race that long in darkness pined

Words: John Morison

Music: Lowell Mason

ZERAH CM extended

1. The race that long in dark-ness pined has seen a glo-rious light; the peo-ple dwell in day, who dwelt in death's sur-round-ing night; the peo-ple dwell in day, who dwelt in death's sur-round - ing night.

2. To hail thy rise, thou better sun,
the gath'ring nations come,
joyous, as when the reapers bear
the harvest-treasures home;
joyous, as when the reapers bear
the harvest-treasures home.

3. To us a child of hope is born,
to us a son is giv'n;
him shall the tribes of earth obey,
him all the hosts of heav'n;
him shall the tribes of earth obey,
him all the hosts of heav'n.

4. His name shall be the Prince of Peace,
for evermore adored;
the Wonderful, the Counsellor,
the great and mighty Lord;
the Wonderful, the Counsellor,
the great and mighty Lord.

5. His pow'r increasing still shall spread;
his reign no end shall know:
justice shall guard his throne above,
and peace abound below;
justice shall guard his throne above,
and peace abound below.

179 There's a special feeling

(It's Christmas time again)

Words and Music: Philip Chapman
and Stephanie Chapman
arr. Dave Bankhead

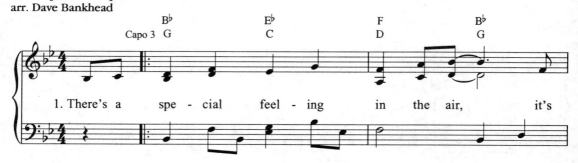

1. There's a spe - cial feel - ing in the air, it's

Christ - mas time a - gain, when from heav'n a - bove God

sent his love when his Son Je - sus came.

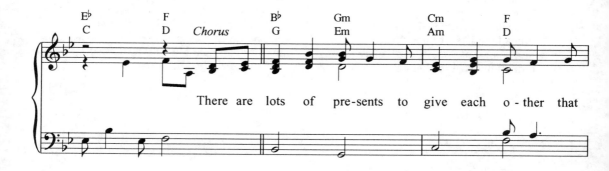

Chorus

There are lots of pre - sents to give each o - ther that

don't need mo-ney at all, when we show our love, when they know we care, that's the best gift we can share. 2. Re - share.

2. Remember all that Jesus brings
   each day the whole year through,
   he gives us help and he gives us love
   and he gave his life for you.

3. So think about the ones you love
   and all that you can do
   to help them feel all your love so real,
   just as Jesus loves you too.

180 There's a star

Words and Music: James Wright
arr. Chris Mitchell

fields are daz - zled by a glo - rious sight, an - gels sing - ing glo - ry to the Sa - viour born this hap - py morn - ing.

2. Wise men travel far to gaze
   and worship at his feet,
   bearing precious gifts before
   the Saviour born this happy morning.

181 There's a star in the East

(Rise up, shepherd, and follow)

Words and Music: American Spiritual
arr. Malcolm Archer

1. There's a star in the East on Christ-mas morn, rise up, shep-herd, and

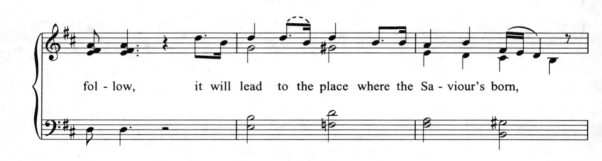

fol - low, it will lead to the place where the Sa - viour's born,

rise up, shep-herd, and fol-low. Leave your sheep and leave your lambs, O

rise up, shep-herd, and fol - low. Leave your ewes and

leave your rams, O rise up, shep-herd, and fol-low.

Fol - low, fol - low, rise up, shep-herd, and fol-low.

Fol - low the star of Beth - le - hem, rise up, shep - herd, and fol - low.

2. If you take good heed of the angel's words,
   rise up, shepherd, and follow,
   you'll forget your flocks you'll forget your herds,
   rise up, shepherd, and follow.

182 There was no room in Bethlehem

Words: Margaret Clarkson

Music: Henry Walford Davies

1. There was no room in Beth-le-hem for him who left his throne to seek the lost at count-less cost and make their griefs his own: but there was room at Cal-va-ry up-on a cross of shame for him to die, up-lift-ed high, and bear the sin-ner's blame.

2. There was no room in Bethlehem,
   and in the world today
   man will not give him room to live
   but bids him turn away;
   but there is room at Calvary,
   and there he stands to give
   a home to all who heed his call
   and look to him and live.

3. There was no room in Bethlehem
   for Christ, the Prince of heav'n
   come down to earth in human birth
   that man might be forgiv'n:
   but there is room at Calvary
   for sinners to abide,
   and all who come will find a home
   in Jesus crucified.

183 The shepherds found the stable *(In the stable)*

Words: Hilda Rostron

Music: Colin Peters
arr. Chris Mitchell

Like a prayer

1. The shep-herds found the sta-ble and saw the ba-by there; they

quiet-ly knelt be-side him and said a 'thank you' prayer. 2. The

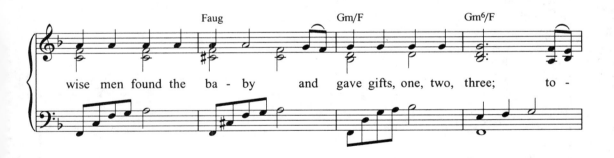

wise men found the ba-by and gave gifts, one, two, three; to-

day it is his birth-day: my gift is – LOVE from me.

184 The Virgin Mary had a baby boy

Words: Traditional West Indian

Music: Traditional West Indian melody
arr. Christopher Tambling

2. The angels sang when the baby was born, *(x3)*
   and proclaimed him the Saviour Jesus.

3. The wise men saw where the baby was born, *(x3)*
   and they saw that his name was Jesus.

185 The wise may bring their learning

Words: Unknown, in this version Word and Music

Music: Tyrolean melody
arr. David Peacock

TYROL DCM

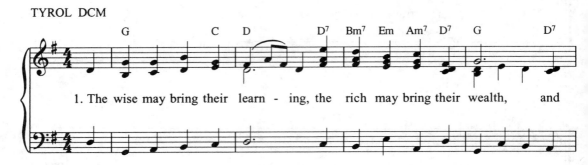

1. The wise may bring their learn - ing, the rich may bring their wealth, and

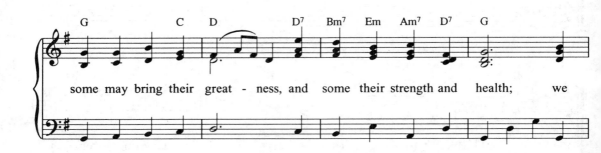

some may bring their great - ness, and some their strength and health; we

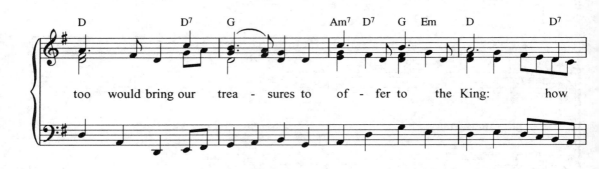

too would bring our trea - sures to of - fer to the King: how

shall we greet our Sa - viour, what pre - sents shall we bring?

2. We'll bring the many duties
   we have to do each day,
   we'll try our best to please him,
   at home, at work, at play;
   and better are these treasures
   to offer to the King,
   than richest gifts without them –
   yet these we all may bring.

3. We'll bring him hearts that love him,
   we'll bring him thankful praise,
   and lives for ever striving
   to follow in his ways;
   and these shall be the treasures
   we offer to the King,
   the gifts that now and ever
   our grateful hearts may bring!

186 The wise men offer their gifts to him

(Worship song)

Words and Music: Mark and Helen Johnson
arr. Chris Mitchell

2. The shepherds tell of their love for him,
Jesus Christ, King of kings,
the shepherds tell of their love for him,
Christ the new-born King.

3. The choir of angels rejoice in him,
Jesus Christ, King of kings,
the choir of angels rejoice in him,
Christ the new-born King.

4. Let's join together to worship him,
Jesus Christ, King of kings,
let's join together to worship him,
Christ the new-born King.

187 This Child

Words and Music: Graham Kendrick

1. This Child, se-cret-ly comes in the night, O this

Child, hi-ding a hea - ven-ly light, O this Child, com-ing to us

like a stran-ger, this hea - ven-ly Child. This

2. This Child, rising on us like the sun,
   O this Child, given to light everyone,
   O this Child, guiding our feet on the pathway
   to peace on earth.

3. This Child, raising the humble and poor,
   O this Child, making the proud ones to fall;
   O this Child, filling the hungry with good things,
   this heavenly Child.

188 Thou didst leave thy throne

Words: Emily Elizabeth Steele Elliot, based on Luke 2:7, adapted by Michael Forster

Music: Timothy Richard Matthews

MARGARET 10 8 11 8 and Refrain

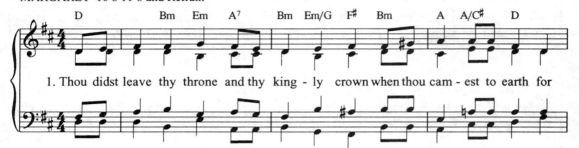

1. Thou didst leave thy throne and thy king - ly crown when thou cam - est to earth for

me, but in Beth - le-hem's home was there found no room for thy

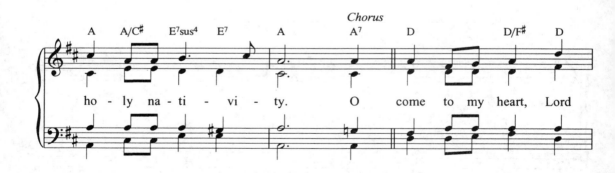

Chorus

ho - ly na - ti - vi - ty. O come to my heart, Lord

Je - sus, there is room in my heart for thee.

2. Heaven's arches rang when the angels sang
   and proclaimed thee of royal degree,
   but in lowliest birth didst thou come to earth
   and in deepest humility.

3. Though the fox found rest, and the bird its nest
   in the shade of the cedar tree,
   yet the world found no bed for the Saviour's head
   in the desert of Galilee.

4. Though thou camest, Lord, with the living word
   that should set all thy people free,
   yet with treachery, scorn and a crown of thorn
   did they bear thee to Calvary.

5. When the heav'ns shall ring and the angels sing
   at thy coming to victory,
   let thy voice call me home, saying, 'Heav'n has room,
   there is room at my side for thee.'

189 Thou who wast rich

Words: Frank Houghton

Music: French carol melody
arr. Chris Mitchell

FRAGRANCE 98 98 98

1. Thou who wast rich be-yond all splen-dour,

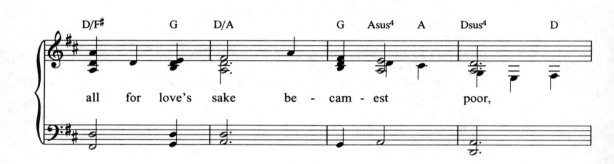

all for love's sake be-cam-est poor,

thrones for a man-ger didst sur-ren-der

sap-phire-paved courts for sta-ble floor.

Thou who wast rich be - yond all splen - dour,

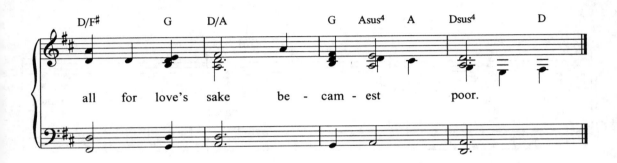

all for love's sake be - cam - est poor.

2. Thou who art God beyond all praising,
   all for love's sake becamest man;
   stooping so low, but sinners raising
   heav'nwards by thine eternal plan.
   Thou who art God beyond all praising,
   all for love's sake becamest man.

3. Thou who art love beyond all telling,
   Saviour and King, we worship thee.
   Immanuel, within us dwelling,
   make us what thou wouldst have us be.
   Thou who art love beyond all telling,
   Saviour and King, we worship thee.

190 Tonight

(Glory to God)

Words and Music: Graham Kendrick

pear!
peared!

(Men) Glo – ry to

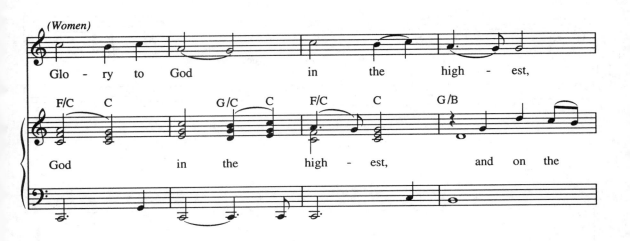

(Women)

Glo – ry to God   in   the   high – est,

God   in   the   high – est,   and   on   the

earth *(All)* be peace from heav'n!   peace from

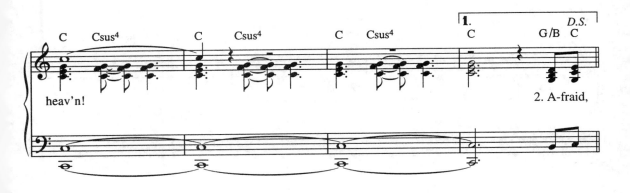

heav'n!   2. A-fraid,

2.

And so to Beth - le - hem

to find it all was true;

des - pised and worth-less shep-herds,

we were the first to know!

(Men) Glo - ry to

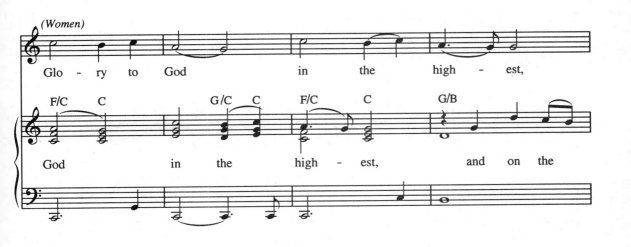

(Women)

Glo - ry to God in the high - est,

F/C · C · G/C · C · F/C · C · G/B

God in the high - est, and on the

Am

1, 3.
D · G

earth (All) be peace from heav'n!

2.
Dm⁷ · G⁷ · C · D.S.

4.
Dm⁷ · G⁷

peace from heav'n! peace from

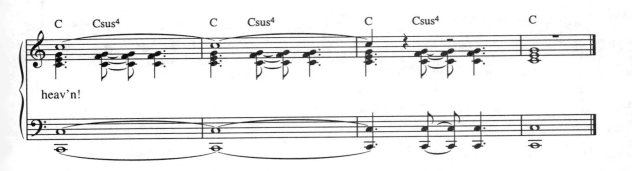

C · Csus⁴ · C · Csus⁴ · C · Csus⁴ · C

heav'n!

191 Two thousand years ago

Words and Music: Mark and Helen Johnson
arr. Chris Mitchell

1. Two thou-sand years a-go, in Beth-le-hem, in Beth-le-hem,
2. Two thou-sand years a-go, he came to us, he came to us,

two thou-sand years a-go a ba-by King was born. *(Repeat verse 1)*
two thou-sand years a-go he came to love us all. *(Repeat verse 2)*

Chorus

Ga-ther round and lis-ten to our Christ-mas sto-ry,

though you've heard it ma-ny times be-fore;

192 Unto us a boy is born

Words: *Puer nobis nascitur*
trans. Percy Dearmer

Music: From *Piae Cantiones*
arr. Adrian Vernon Fish

PUER NOBIS 76 77

1. Un-to us a boy is born! King of all cre-a-tion; came he to a

world for-lorn, the Lord of ev-'ry na-tion, the Lord of ev-'ry na-tion.

2. Cradled in a stall was he,
   watched by cows and asses;
   but the very beasts could see
   that he the world surpasses,
   that he the world surpasses.

3. Then the fearful Herod cried,
   'Pow'r is mine in Jewry!'
   So the blameless children died
   the victims of his fury,
   the victims of his fury.

4. Now may Mary's Son, who came
   long ago to love us,
   lead us all with hearts aflame
   unto the joys above us,
   unto the joys above us.

5. Omega and Alpha he!
   Let the organ thunder,
   while the choir with peals of glee
   shall rend the air asunder,
   shall rend the air asunder.

193 Unto us a child is born

Words and Music: Mark Johnson and Helen Johnson
arr. Dave Bankhead

day in Beth - le -hem   the love of   God   has come   to men,   the

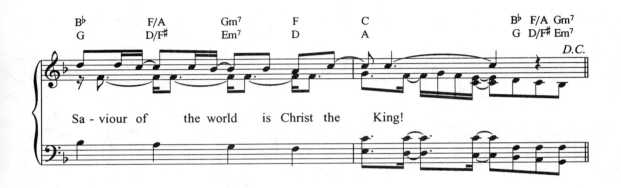

Sa - viour of   the world   is Christ the   King!

2. Leave your cares aside,
   seek and you will find,
   for today in Bethlehem
   the love of God has come to men,
   the Saviour of the world is Jesus Christ!

3. Come, let us adore,
   now and evermore,
   for today in Bethlehem
   the love of God has come to men,
   the Saviour of the world is Christ the Lord!

194 We have some news to bring

Words and Music: Greg Leavers
arr. Chris Mitchell

We have some news to bring and so this song we'll sing, that a

babe's been born who is a hea-ven-ly king. And the mes-sage we bring is that

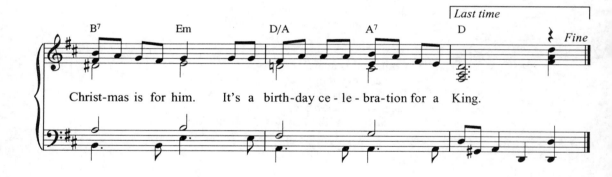

Christ-mas is for him. It's a birth-day ce-le-bra-tion for a King.

To continue

King. 1. Je-sus was born in a sta -

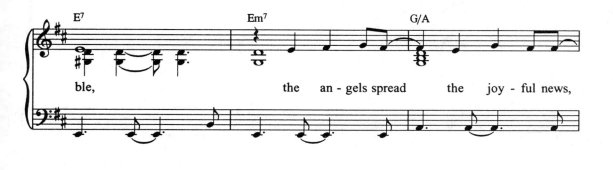

the an - gels spread the joy - ful news,

the an - gels spread the joy - ful news,

Now we can sing it a - gain! We have some

2. Shepherds came down from the hillside
to worship Christ, the new-born King,
to worship Christ, the new-born King.
Now we can sing it again!

3. A star led wise men to Jesus,
they brought gold, frankincense and myrrh,
they brought gold, frankincense and myrrh.
Now we can sing it again!

195 Welcome the Christ-child

Words and Music: F. Roy Bennett

Crisp tango rhythm

1. Wel - come the Christ - child,
2. Shep - herds on hill - sides

Je - sus our Sa - viour, born for us all this day:
hear of his com - ing, swift - ly they leave their fold;

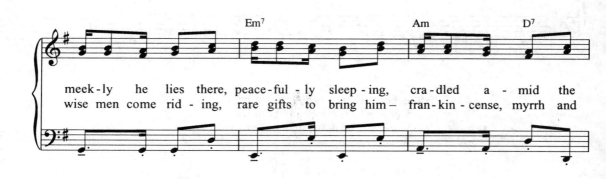

meek - ly he lies there, peace - ful - ly sleep - ing, cra - dled a - mid the
wise men come rid - ing, rare gifts to bring him— fran - kin - cense, myrrh and

hay. Come now be - fore him, kneel and a - dore him,
gold. Hea - ven is ring - ing, an - gels are sing - ing,

hon - our the King of kings; wel-come the Christ - child,
tell - ing of Je - sus' birth: wel-come the Christ - child,

born in the man - ger — glad-ness and joy he brings!
born in the man - ger, king of all heav'n and earth.

196 We three kings of Orient are

Words: John Henry Hopkins alt.

Music: John Henry Hopkins

KINGS OF ORIENT 88 86 and Refrain

1. We three kings of O - ri - ent are;   bear - ing gifts we tra - verse a - far;

field   and foun - tain, moor and moun - tain, fol - low - ing yon - der star.

Chorus

O   star of won - der, star of night,   star with roy - al beau - ty bright,

west - ward lead - ing, still pro - ceed - ing, guide us   to   thy per - fect light.

2. Born a King on Bethlehem plain,
   gold I bring, to crown him again,
   King for ever, ceasing never,
   over us all to reign.

3. Frankincense to offer have I,
   incense owns a Deity nigh,
   prayer and praising, gladly raising,
   worship him, God most high.

4. Myrrh is mine, its bitter perfume
   breathes a life of gathering gloom;
   sorrowing, sighing, bleeding, dying,
   sealed in the stone-cold tomb.

5. Glorious now behold him arise,
   King and God and sacrifice;
   alleluia, alleluia,
   earth to heav'n replies.

197 We were not there

Words: Paul Wigmore

Music: Austrian folk melody
arr. Simon Anderson

198 We will sing your song
(You came from the highest)

Words and Music: Graham Kendrick

We will sing your song, fol-low you for e - ver. We will be your hands reach-ing out a - gain. Your song goes on and on, your laugh-ter breaks the sil - ence. The sea - son of your joy will ne - ver, ne - ver end.

1. You came from the high-est, reached down to the low-est,

reach - ing out a - gain. Your song goes on and on, your laugh - ter breaks the sil - ence. The sea - son of your joy will ne - ver, ne - ver end. And ne - ver, ne - ver end.

2. You came from the kindest,
   to suffer the cruellest,
   you are the message of love.
   You came from the purest,
   to die for the foulest,
   you are the message of love.
   Our God unrecognised,
   for ruined sinners crucified.

3. In the bustle of main street,
   the noise and the concrete,
   make us your message of love.
   In the turmoil of nations,
   or a heart's desperation,
   make us your message of love.
   Each step, each breath we take,
   yours is the love we celebrate.

199 We wish you a merry Christmas

Words: Traditional English

Music: Traditional English
arr. Neil Jenkins

1. We wish you a mer-ry Christ-mas, we wish you a mer-ry

Christ-mas, we wish you a mer-ry Christ-mas and a hap-py New Year.

Chorus

Good ti-dings we bring to you and your kin. We

Last time Fine

wish you a mer-ry Christ-mas and a hap-py New Year.

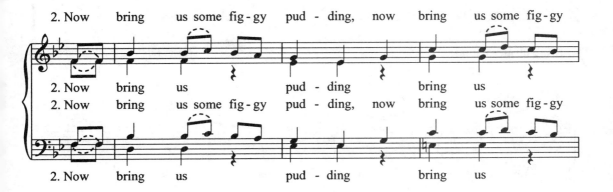

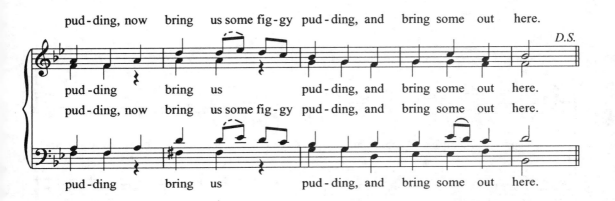

Soprano and Tenor words	Alto and Bass words
3. For we all like figgy pudding, we all like figgy pudding, we all like figgy pudding, so bring some out here.	3. For we all like ..... pudding, ... all like ..... pudding, ... all like ..... pudding, so bring some out here.
4. And we won't go until we've got some, we won't go until we've got some, we won't go until we've got some, so bring some out here.	4. And we won't go ..... got some, ... won't go ..... got some, ... won't go ..... got some, so bring some out here.

200 What child is this

Words: William Chatterton Dix

Music: English traditional melody

GREENSLEEVES 87 87 and Refrain

1. What child is this, who, laid to rest, on Ma - ry's lap is

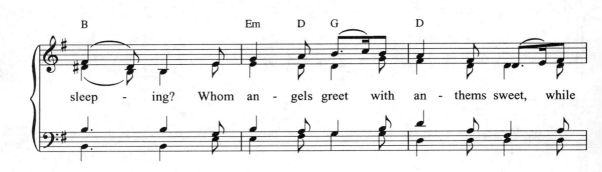

sleep - ing? Whom an - gels greet with an - thems sweet, while

shep - herds watch are keep - ing? *Chorus* This, this is

Christ the King, whom shep - herds guard and an - gels sing:

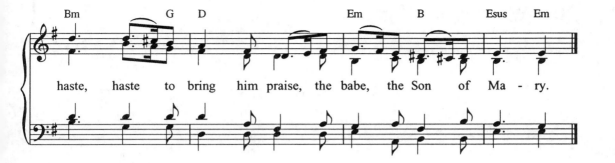

haste, haste to bring him praise, the babe, the Son of Ma - ry.

2. Why lies he in such mean estate,
   where ox and ass are feeding?
   Good Christian fear: for sinners here
   the silent Word is pleading.

3. So bring him incense, gold, and myrrh,
   come, peasant, king, to own him.
   The King of kings salvation brings,
   let loving hearts enthrone him.

201 What kind of greatness

Words and Music: Graham Kendrick

2. The One in whom we live and move
   in swaddling clothes lies bound.
   The voice that cried 'Let there be light!',
   asleep without a sound.
   The One who strode among the stars,
   and called each one by name,
   lies helpless in a mother's arms
   and must learn to walk again.

3. What greater love could he have shown
   to shamed humanity?
   Yet human pride hates to believe
   in such deep humility.
   But nations now may see his grace
   and know that he is near,
   when his meek heart, his words, his works
   are incarnate in us here.

202 What was it like for the shepherds

Words: Mary Wright

Music: Roger Jones arr. Donald Thomson

Capo 3

1. What was it like for the shep - herds, out on the hills in the night? What was it like for the shep - herds, on see - ing the bright shin-ing light? (*Shout*) Hear the an - gels!

Chorus Glo - ry! Glo - ry! Glo - ry to God on high!

Glo - ry! Glo - ry!

Glo - ry to God on high!

To repeat

To end

D.C.

2. What was it like for the shepherds,
   seeing an angel out there?
   What was it like for the shepherds,
   so scared by the sudden bright glare?

3. What was it like for the shepherds,
   leaving their sheep in the cold?
   What was it like for the shepherds,
   to do as the angel had told?

4. There was great joy for the shepherds,
   leaving their fields cold and wild!
   There was great joy for the shepherds
   on seeing the newly born child.

203 When God from heaven to earth came down

Words: Michael Perry

Music: Traditional English melody
arr. Simon Anderson

I SAW THREE SHIPS 88 88

1. When God from heav'n to earth came down on

Christ - mas Day, on Christ - mas Day, the songs rang out in

Beth - le'm town on Christ - mas Day in the morn - ing.

Sopranos
2. For Christ was born to save us all,
   on Christmas Day, on Christmas Day,
   and laid within a manger stall
   on Christmas Day in the morning.

Men
3. The shepherds heard the angels sing
   on Christmas Day, on Christmas Day,
   to tell them of the saviour-king
   on Christmas Day in the morning.

All
4. Now joy is ours and all is well,
   on Christmas Day, on Christmas Day,
   so sound the organ, chime the bell
   on Christmas Day in the morning!

204 When he comes

Words and Music: Sue Read
arr. Andy Silver and Christopher Norton

1. When he comes we'll see just a child; no war-rior

lord but a ba-by so mild. The Lord says:

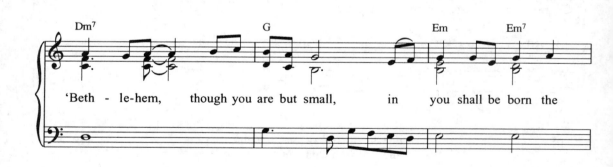

'Beth - le-hem, though you are but small, in you shall be born the

King.' When he comes, when he comes.

2. When he comes his reign shall bring peace; when he

comes all fight - ing shall cease. Men shall

ham - mer their spears in - to pru - ning hooks and pre - pare for bat - tle no more.

When he comes, when he comes. And on that

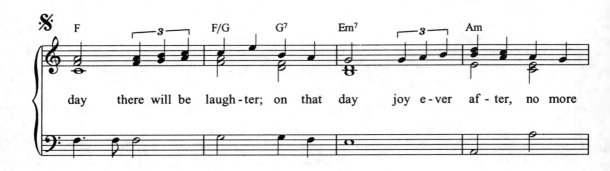

day   there will be laugh-ter; on that day   joy e-ver af - ter, no more

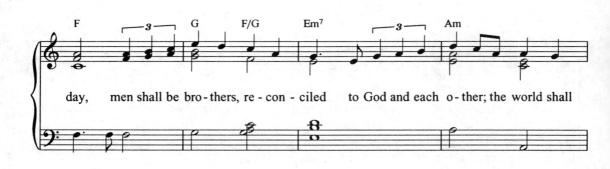

tears: for the Lord will wipe them   all   a-way.   And on that

day,   men shall be bro-thers, re - con - ciled   to God and each o-ther; the world shall

see   the King in his glo - ry, when   he   comes.

3. When he comes he'll be of Da-vid's line, the migh-ty

God and ru - ler di - vine. They'll call him

Won - der - ful and Coun-sel-lor, and his king-dom shall ne-ver cease.

When he comes, when he comes. And on that

205 When the angel came to Mary

Words: Michael Perry,
based on the traditional carol

Music: Cornish traditional melody
arr. Simon Anderson

1.When the an-gel came to Ma-ry, he said, 'Be at peace, for the

Lord God shall be with you, his love will not cease.' And

Ma-ry bore Je-sus Christ, our sa-viour for to be; and the

first and the last and the great-est is he, is he, is

he; and the first and the last and the great-est is he.

2. When the angel came to Mary,
   he said, 'Do not fear,
   for his pow'r shall be upon you,
   a child you will bear.'

3. When the angel came to Mary,
   he said, 'Hear his name,
   for his title shall be Jesus
   of kingly acclaim.'

4. When the angel came to Mary,
   she said, 'Be it so:
   for the Lord God is my master,
   his will I must do.'

206 While shepherds watched

Words: Nahum Tate, alt.

Music: from Este's *Psalter*

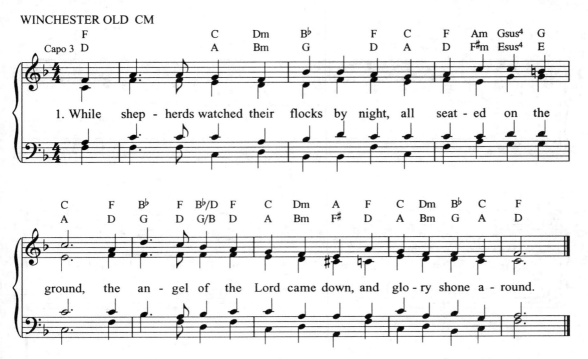

2. 'Fear not,' said he, (for mighty dread
   had seized their troubled mind);
   'glad tidings of great joy I bring
   to you and all mankind.

3. 'To you in David's town this day
   is born of David's line
   a Saviour, who is Christ the Lord;
   and this shall be the sign:

4. 'The heav'nly babe you there shall find
   to human view displayed,
   all meanly wrapped in swathing bands,
   and in a manger laid.'

5. Thus spake the seraph, and forthwith
   appeared a shining throng
   of angels praising God, who thus
   addressed their joyful song:

6. 'All glory be to God on high,
   and to the earth be peace,
   goodwill henceforth from heav'n to earth
   begin and never cease.'

207 Whiter than the snow

Words and Music: Mike Burn

208 Who is he, in yonder stall

Benjamin Russell Hanby

WHO IS HE 77 and Refrain

1. Who is he, in yon-der stall, at whose feet the shep-herds fall? 'Tis the Lord! O won-drous sto-ry! 'Tis the Lord! the King of Glo-ry! At his feet we hum-bly fall; crown him, crown him Lord of all.

2. Who is he, in yonder cot,
bending to his toilsome lot?

3. Who is he, in deep distress,
fasting in the wilderness?

4. Who is he, that stands and weeps
at the grave where Laz'rus sleeps?

5. Lo, at midnight, who is he
prays in dark Gethsemane?

6. Who is he, in Calv'ry's throes,
asks for blessings on his foes?

7. Who is he that from the grave
comes to heal and help and save?

8. Who is he that from his throne
rules through all the worlds alone?

209 Wonderful counsellor

Words and Music: Chick Yuill

Moderato(♩ = 108)

1. Won-der-ful coun-sel-lor, migh-ty God a-mong us,
2. Son of God, Son of Man, Word of God in-car-nate,
3. King of kings, Lord of lords, Son of God ex-alt-ed;

e-ver-last-ing Fa-ther, Prince who rules in peace. To
suff-'ring Sa-viour, glo-ri-ous ris-en Lord. For
name a-bove ev-'ry name, Lamb up-on the throne. This

us a child is born, to us a son is giv'n, to
God so loved the world he gave his on-ly son; no
king will come a-gain, the Fa-ther's on-ly son; no

those who walked in dark-ness the light has come.
more we walk in dark-ness, the light has come.
more a world in dark-ness, the light will come.

210 Wonderful counsellor, the mighty God

Words and Music: Paul Armstrong

won - der - ful   coun - sel - lor,   won - der - ful

is the name of Je - sus,   won - der - ful

coun - sel - lor,   won - der - ful   coun - sel - lor,

won - der - ful   is the name of Je - sus.

indexes

Index of Songwriters, Authors, Composers and Arrangers

Ainger, Geoffrey 16
Alexander, Cecil Frances 146
Anderson, Simon 9, 197, 203, 205
Anschütz, Ernst 137
Archer, Malcolm 125, 181
Armstrong, Paul 210

Bach, Johann Sebastian 17, 144
Baker, Henry William 141
Baker, Marilyn 61
Bankhead, Dave 50, 79, 130, 179, 193
Baring-Gould, Sabine 168, 172
Baughen, Michael 84
Beethoven, Ludwig van 73, 106
Bennett, F. Roy 195
Booth-Clibborn, William E. 45
Boswell, Eric 115
Bradley, Heather 11
Bradley, Laura 11
Brahms, Johannes 119
Brooks, Phillips 145
Burch, Trevor 155
Burn, Mike 207
Burt, Phil 38, 52, 84
Bush, Emma F. 82
Byrom, John 26

Capua, Eduardo di 45
Carpenter, Margaret 79
Caswall, Edward 159
Chapman, Phil 67
Chapman, Philip 130, 179
Chapman, Stephanie 130, 179
Chesterton, Frances 86
Chisholm, Emily 175
Clark, Jodi Page 41
Clarkson, Margaret 46, 182
Collison, Valerie 32
Cook, Joseph Simpson 57
Cooke, Dave 23
Croo, Robert 126
Crüger, Johann 69, 177
Cullen, Tim 72
Cummings, William Hayman 75
Cunningham, Tom 174

Davies, Henry Walford 182
Day, Hilda M. 135
Dearmer Percy 116, 144, 192
Dix, William Chatterton 12, 200
Doddridge, Philip 74
Dudley-Smith, Timothy 25, 35, 38, 84, 161
Dunman, S. J. P. 40
Dyke, Henry van 106

Ebeling, Johann Georg 5
Elliot, Emily Elizabeth Steele 124, 188
Este's Psalter 206

Faircloth, Alta C. 76
Fellingham, Dave 49
Fish, Adrian Vernon 175, 192
Fishel, Donald 176
Forster, Michael 14, 80, 146, 188

Gauntlett, Henry John 146
Gerhardt, Paul 5
Golby, Ivor 1
Goss, John 159
Green, Fred Pratt 118
Grüber, Franz 164

Hadden, David 51
Hairston, Jester 120
Hanby, Benjamin Russell 208
Hand, Colin 24, 44, 90, 140, 164
Handel, George Frideric 108
Harding, Nick 129
Hare, Susie 55, 133, 155
Hearn, Naida 104
Heber, Reginald 18
Heller, Ruth 137
Helmore, Thomas 140
Herrington, Paul 113
Hodges, Edward 106
Holst, Gustav 91
Hopkins, John Henry 196
Houghton, Frank 189
Howard, Pat Uhl 150

Jackson, Francis 93
Jenkins, Neil 43, 86, 94, 126, 137, 199
Johnson, Anne 113
Johnson, Helen 50, 71, 89, 111, 162, 186, 191, 193
Johnson, Mark 50, 71, 89, 111, 162, 186, 191, 193
Jones, Roger 99, 156, 202

Kendrick, Graham 3, 7, 13, 20, 21, 42, 47, 54, 66, 77, 78, 87, 88, 92, 107, 114, 122, 131, 134, 136, 139, 147, 151, 154, 158, 165, 166, 170, 187, 190, 198, 201
Kirkpatrick, William James 14
Knight, Mollie 73
Kocher, Conrad 12

Lawton, Joan 109
Leavers, Greg 60, 167, 194
Leckebusch, Martin E. 177
Levell, Susanna 6
Lloyd, Richard 14, 118, 172

MacBean, Lachlan 24
MacDonald, Mary 24
Macpherson, J. 100
Madan, Martin 75
Marshall-Taylor, Geoffrey 33

Mason, Lowell 178
Matthews, Timothy Richard 124, 188
Mawson, Linda 163
Mayor, Roger 105
McGee, Bob 48
Mendelssohn, Felix 75
Mitchell, Chris 6, 11, 19, 27, 28, 29, 31, 33, 36, 48, 57, 58, 60, 67, 68, 70, 71, 82, 89, 96, 97, 99, 101, 103, 112, 119, 120, 121, 123, 127, 128, 129, 132, 141, 143, 149, 157, 161, 162, 167, 169, 171, 177, 180, 183, 186, 189, 191, 194
Mohr, Joseph 164
Monk, Edwin George 10
Monk, William Henry 12, 69
Monsell, John Samuel Bewley 152
Montgomery, James 8, 69
Moody, Dave 4
Moore, Andrew 115
Moore, Philip 168
Morison, John 178
Morris, Reginald Owen 125
Mowbray, David 93
Murray, James R. 14

Neale, John Mason 2, 64, 65, 140, 141
Newton, John 7
Niles, John Jacob 98
Norton, Christopher 151, 204

Oakeley, Frederick 138
Overton, Phil 19
Owens, Carol 29
Owens, Jimmy 29, 81

Peace, Albert Lister 15
Peacock, David 41, 61, 102, 113, 117, 122, 185
Perry, Michael 53, 101, 102, 105, 157, 160, 203, 205
Pestel, Thomas 15
Peters, Colin 183
Piae Cantiones 57, 65, 101, 118, 141, 192
Pott, Francis 10
Praetorius, Michael 2
Price, Alan 30, 31, 171
Prudentius, Aurelius Clemens 141
Puckett, Martha 22
Puckett, Paul E. 22
Pulkingham, Betty 150, 176

Ravenscroft, Thomas 74
Rawsthorne, Noel 80
Read, Sue 204
Reed, Edith Margaret Gellibrand 90
Rees, Bryn Austin 174
Rettino, Debbie 28

Rettino, Ernie 28
Rist, Johann 17
Robinson, Joan 149
Rossetti, Christina Georgina 91, 125
Rostron, Hilda 183
Rowe, George Stringer 40
Ruddle, Valerie 25
Russell, A. T. 17

Sandy, William 94, 173
Sankey 103
Sankey, Ira D. 36
Sargent, Malcolm 58
Savage, Jonathan 107, 147
Scheidt, Samuel 144
Schop, Johann 17
Schulz, Johann A. P. 142
Sears, Edward Hamilton 95
Shaw, Martin 116, 144
Sibelius, Jean 35, 83
Silver, Andy 128, 204
St Germanus 2
Stainer, John 37, 62, 64, 65, 173
Stone, David 113
Sturdy, Leslie 121
Sullivan, Arthur Seymour 95

Tambling, Christopher 116, 160, 184
Tate, Nahum 206
Thomson, Donald 39, 111, 156, 202
Thrupp, Joseph Francis 18
Townend, Stuart 56
Troutbeck, John 17
Turner, R. N. 36

Verrall, Pamela 117

Waddington, S. P. 34
Wade, John Francis 138
Wainwright, John 26
Warren, Norman 53
Warren, Philip 85
Watts Isaac 108
Webb, Joy 97
Wesley, Charles 37, 59, 75, 110
Wesley, John 59
White, Ian 39
Whitefield, George 75
Wigmore, Paul 197
Williams, Ralph Vaughan 63, 145, 148
Winkworth, Catherine 5
Witt, Christian Friedrich 37
Wood, Charles 44, 153
Woodward, George Ratcliffe 44, 153
Wright, James 27, 70, 96, 112, 123, 143, 169, 180
Wright, Mary 202

Young, John Freeman 164
Yuill, Chick 209

Scriptural Index

GENESIS

| 22:8 | See, amid the winter's snow | 159 |
| | The promised time arrives | 177 |

EXODUS

3:14	Down from his glory	45
	Glory be to God on high	59
19:16-20	O come, O come Emmanuel	140

NUMBERS

| 6:22-27 | Peace to you | 154 |
| 21:4 | There was no room in Bethlehem | 182 |

DEUTERONOMY

| 4:29 | O come and join the dance | 139 |

2 SAMUEL

7:12-16	Hail to the Lord's anointed	69
7:12	Into darkness light has broken	93
	The promised time arrives	177

JOB

| 38:7 | Angels from the realms of glory | 8 |

PSALMS

2:7	Of the Father's heart begotten	141
4:7	Joy to the world	108
16:11	Ain't nothing like it	3
	Joy to the world	108
	Now dawns the sun of righteousness	136
19:1	Joyful, joyful we adore thee	106
45:7	O little one sweet, O little one mild	144
46:1-7	Emmanuel, God with us	49
46:11	Emmanuel, God with us	49
50:23	The wise may bring their learning	185
51:7-8	God came among us	61
51:17	Brightest and best	18
	O worship the Lord in the beauty of holiness	152
55:22	O come and join the dance	139
	O worship the Lord in the beauty of holiness	152
57:7-11	Joy to all the world	107
65:13	Joy to the world	108
72:1-19	Hail to the Lord's anointed	69
72:1-8	He is born, our Lord and Saviour	81
72:1	Into darkness light has broken	93
72:8-9	The race that long in darkness pined	178
72:19	Holy, holy Lord	85
93:3-4	Joy to the world	108
95:1	Sing, all the earth	166
96:1	Sing, all the earth	166
96:9	Brightest and best	18
	O worship the Lord in the beauty of holiness	152
96:10-14	Joy to the world	108
100:1-2	Joy to all the world	107
	Joy to the world	108
103:20-22	Of the Father's heart begotten	141
119:105	Darkness like a shroud	42
126:1	Can you believe it?	20
126:1-2	In the firelight	92
	Now dawns the sun of righteousness	136
	When he comes	204

PROVERBS

| 12:10 | Hee, haw! Hee, haw! | 80 |

ISAIAH

1:18	God came among us	61
	Whiter than the snow	207
2:3	The race that long in darkness pined	178
2:4	Now dawns the sun of righteousness	136
	When he comes	204
6:3	Holy, holy Lord	85
7:14	A great and mighty wonder	2
	All hail King Jesus!	4
	Call his name	19
	Can you believe it?	20
	C is for the Christ Child	23
	Child in the manger	24
	Come and join the celebration	32
	Come, come, come to the manger	34
	Come now with awe	35
	Come sing the sweet song of the ages	36
	Emmanuel	48
	Emmanuel, God with us	49
	From the squalor of a borrowed stable	56
	Glory be to God on high	59
	Hark, the herald-angels sing	75
	Immanuel, God is with us	87
	Into darkness light has broken	93
	Jesus, name above all names	104
	Let earth and heaven combine	110
	Let me tell you about a baby	111
	Let there be singing	112
	Like a candle flame	114
	Look to the skies	122
	O come, O come Emmanuel	140
	O little town of Bethlehem	145
	Silently we watch	163
	Since the day the angel came	165
	The angel Gabriel from heaven came	172
	Thou who wast rich	189
	Unto us a child is born	193
9:2	Good news	66
9:2-7	Now dawns the sun of righteousness	136
9:2	O come and join the dance	139
	O come, O come Emmanuel	140
	On Christmas night all Christians sing	148
9:2-3	The race that long in darkness pined	178
9:2	Wonderful counsellor	209
9:6	Can you believe it?	20
	Carols sing	22
	Child in the manger	24
	Come now with awe	35
	Come sing the sweet song of the ages	36
	Cradle rocking	41
9:6-7	For unto us a child is born	51
9:6	For unto us a child is born	52
	Glory be to God on high	59
	God came among us	61
	Happy day of great rejoicing	73
	Hark, the herald-angels sing	75
	Hear the sound of people singing	77
	He is born, our Lord and Saviour	81
	His name, his name	83
	Holy, holy Lord	85
	Immanuel, God is with us	87
	Into darkness light has broken	93
	It came upon the midnight clear	95
	Look to the skies	122
	Peace to you	154
	People awaken, open your eyes	155
	Rumours of angels	158
	See, to us a child is born	161
	Silently we watch	163
	Since the day the angel came	165

Isaiah

9:6	So many centuries	170
	The race that long in darkness pined	178
	Unto us a child is born	193
	When he comes	204
	Wonderful counsellor	209
	Wonderful counsellor, the mighty God	210
11:1-5	O come, O come Emmanuel	140
22:22	O come, O come Emmanuel	140
35:5-6	In the firelight	92
40:1-2	O little one sweet, O little one mild	144
40:9	Joy to all the world	107
43:18-19	Can you believe it?	20
53:3	Down from his glory	45
	Earth gave him no welcome	46
	Since the day the angel came	165
53:3-6	Whiter than the snow	207
53:4-5	Hallelujah, my Father	72
53:4	He is born, our Lord and Saviour	81
53:4-5	Immanuel, O Immanuel	88
53:4-6	There was no room in Bethlehem	182
53:4	Wonderful counsellor	209
53:11	From heaven you came	54
55:12	Joy to the world	108
57:15	Angel-voices ever singing	10
58:6-7	Amazing grace!	7
60:1-3	Darkness like a shroud	42
60:1-2	Earth lies spellbound	47
60:3	He is born, our Lord and Saviour	81
61:1-3	From the squalor of a borrowed stable	56
	Good King Wenceslas	65
	Hark, the glad sound!	74
	He is born, our Lord and Saviour	81
61:1	In the firelight	92
61:1-3	Once in royal David's city	146
61:10	Whiter than the snow	207

JEREMIAH

29:13	O come and join the dance	139
31:31-33	Long ago, prophets knew	118

DANIEL

7:13	Come and praise the Lord our King	33

MICAH

4:2	The race that long in darkness pined	178
4:3	Now dawns the sun of righteousness	136
	When he comes	204
5:2	Come now with awe	35
	Earth lies spellbound	47
	Let me tell you about a baby	111
	Oh town of Bethlehem	143
	O little town of Bethlehem	145
	Once in royal David's city	146
	When he comes	204

HAGGAI

2:7	Come, thou long-expected Jesus	37

MALACHI

3:1	Angels from the realms of glory	8
4:2	Can you believe it?	20
	Hark, the herald-angels sing	75
	Now dawns the sun of righteousness	136
	People awaken, open your eyes	155

MATTHEW

1:18-25	Call his name	19

Matthew

1:18-19	Jesus born in Bethlehem	100
1:21	A long time ago	6
1:21	Come, thou long-expected Jesus	37
	Down from his glory	45
	From heaven above	53
	From the squalor of a borrowed stable	56
	Glory be to God on high	59
	Good Christian people	63
	Good Christians all, rejoice	64
	Hark, the glad sound!	74
	Hark to the story	76
	Holy, holy Lord	85
	Jesus, baby Jesus	99
	Jesus, name above all names	104
	Let me tell you about a baby	111
	Long ago, prophets knew	118
	Mary had a baby	127
	The Virgin Mary had a baby boy	184
	When God from earth to heaven came down	203
1:23	All hail King Jesus!	4
	A long time ago	6
	Break forth, O beauteous heavenly light	17
	Can you believe it?	20
	C is for the Christ Child	23
	Come and join the celebration	32
	Come, come, come to the manger	34
	Come sing the sweet song of the ages	36
	Cradle rocking	41
	Emmanuel	48
	Emmanuel, God with us	49
	From the squalor of a borrowed stable	56
	Glory be to God on high	59
	Hark, the herald-angels sing	75
	Immanuel, God is with us	87
	Into darkness light has broken	93
	Jesus, name above all names	104
	Let earth and heaven combine	110
	Let there be singing	112
	Like a candle flame	114
	Look to the skies	122
	O come, O come Emmanuel	140
	O little town of Bethlehem	145
	Silently we watch	163
	Since the day the angel came	165
	The angel Gabriel from heaven came	172
	Thou who wast rich	189
	Unto us a child is born	193
2:1-12	A baby was born in Bethlehem	1
	A long time ago	6
	Angels from the realms of glory	8
	A special star	11
	As with gladness men of old	12
	Behold, the great Creator makes	15
	Brightest and best	18
	Carols sing	22
	C is for the Christ Child	23
	Come and join the celebration	32
	Come, watch with us	38
	Gentle Mary laid her child	57
	Hallelu, hallelu, hallelujah	70
	I wonder as I wander	98
2:1-18	Jesus Christ the Lord is born	101
	Kings came riding	109
2:1-12	Little donkey	115
	Look away to Bethlehem	121
	Mary, Joseph, manger and straw	129
	O come, all ye faithful	138
	Past three o'clock	153
	Riding high and low	156
	Shepherds found him	162
	The first nowell	173
	There's a star	180

2:1-12	The shepherds found the stable	183
	The Virgin Mary had a baby boy	184
	The wise may bring their learning	185
	The wise men offer their gifts to him	186
	We have some news to bring	194
	Welcome the Christ-child	195
	We three kings of Orient are	196
2:2	Come, come, come to the manger	34
	Cradle rocking	41
	Glory to God in the highest	60
	Joy to the world	108
	Over the world this Christmas morn	149
2:5-6	Once in royal David's city	146
2:11	At this time of giving	13
	Every Christmas	50
	Here we go to Bethlehem	82
	Holy child	84
	How far is it to Bethlehem?	86
	Journey to Bethlehem	105
	O worship the Lord in the beauty of holiness	152
	The promised time arrives	177
	What child is this?	200
2:16-18	C is for the Christ Child	23
	Lully, lulla, thou little tiny child	126
	Unto us a boy is born	192
3:1-3	The holly and the ivy	175
4:12	Who is he, in yonder stall	208
4:17	Journey to Bethlehem	105
4:19	Christians, awake!	26
	We will sing your song	198
4:23	Jesus born in Bethlehem	100
5:14-16	Darkness like a shroud	42
5:16	Like a candle flame	114
	What kind of greatness	201
5:48	Let earth and heaven combine	110
6:10	Come, thou long-expected Jesus	37
	Darkness like a shroud	42
	Look to the skies	122
7:7	O come and join the dance	139
	Unto us a child is born	193
8:20	Lord, you left your throne	124
	Thou didst leave thy throne	188
8:23-27	Child of the stable's secret birth	25
8:23-26	Jesus born in Bethlehem	100
9:24	Can you believe it?	20
9:36	God came among us	61
10:34	Cradle rocking	41
10:42	Amazing grace!	7
11:19	From the squalor of a borrowed stable	56
11:28-30	It came upon the midnight clear	95
11:28	O come and join the dance	139
11:29	Meekness and majesty	131
12:21	Journey to Bethlehem	105
12:28	The promised time arrives	177
18:20	Angel-voices ever singing	10
19:14	Once upon a universe	147
20:22	Child of the stable's secret birth	25
20:28	From heaven you came	54
22:1-10	Heaven invites you to a party	78
24:14	Now dawns the sun of righteousness	136
24:36	Earth lies spellbound	47
	From the squalor of a borrowed stable	56
24:42	Born in the night, Mary's child	16
25:31-46	Amazing grace!	7
	We will sing your song	198
26:26-28	O what a gift!	150
26:36	Who is he, in yonder stall	208
26:39	Child of the stable's secret birth	25
	From heaven you came	54
26:47-50	No room at the world	134
	Thou didst leave thy throne	188
27:29	Child of the stable's secret birth	25

27:29	In the firelight	92
27:35	Child of the stable's secret birth	25
	Come and praise the Lord our King	33
	From heaven you came	54
	From the heights of glory	55
	From the squalor of a borrowed stable	56
	Jesus born in Bethlehem	100
	Jesus, my Saviour	103
	Lord, you left your throne	124
	Meekness and majesty	131
	No room at the world	134
	No room for the Saviour	135
	O what a gift!	150
	Since the day the angel came	165
	Sing lullaby!	168
	There was no room in Bethlehem	182
	Thou didst leave thy throne	188
	Who is he, in yonder stall	208
27:59-60	No room for the Saviour	135
28:6	Come and praise the Lord our King	33
	From the heights of glory	55
	God came among us	61
	Jesus born in Bethlehem	100
	O what a gift!	150
	Sing lullaby!	168
	Who is he, in yonder stall	208
28:20	Come and praise the Lord our King	33
	Emmanuel	48
	Emmanuel, God with us	49

MARK

1:1-3	The holly and the ivy	175
1:12-13	Who is he, in yonder stall	208
1:17	Christians, awake!	26
	We will sing your song	198
1:32-34	Jesus born in Bethlehem	100
3:13-19	Jesus born in Bethlehem	100
4:35-41	Child of the stable's secret birth	25
4:35-40	Jesus born in Bethlehem	100
10:38	Child of the stable's secret birth	25
10:45	Can you see what we have made?	21
	Child in the manger	24
	Christians, awake!	26
	Earth gave him no welcome	46
	From heaven you came	54
	From the squalor of a borrowed stable	56
	God came among us	61
	He is born, our Lord and Saviour	81
	I wonder as I wander	98
	Jesus, my Saviour	103
	The promised time arrives	177
10:46-52	Amazing grace!	7
14:22-24	O what a gift!	150
14:32	Who is he, in yonder stall	208
14:36	Child of the stable's secret birth	25
	From heaven you came	54
14:43-46	No room at the world	134
	Thou didst leave thy throne	188
15:17	Child of the stable's secret birth	25
	In the firelight	92
15:25	Child of the stable's secret birth	25
	Come and praise the Lord our King	33
	From heaven you came	54
	From the heights of glory	55
	From the squalor of a borrowed stable	56
	Jesus born in Bethlehem	100
	Jesus, my Saviour	103
	Lord, you left your throne	124
	Meekness and majesty	131
	No room at the world	134
	No room for the Saviour	135

Mark

15:25	O what a gift!	150
	Since the day the angel came	165
	Sing lullaby!	168
	There was no room in Bethlehem	182
	Thou didst leave thy throne	188
	Who is he, in yonder stall	208
15:46	No room for the Saviour	135
16:6	Come and praise the Lord our King	33
	From the heights of glory	55
	God came among us	61
	Jesus born in Bethlehem	100
	O what a gift!	150
	Sing lullaby!	168
	Who is he, in yonder stall	208

LUKE

1:26-38	A long time ago	6
	Call his name	19
	From the squalor of a borrowed stable	56
	Let me tell you about a baby	111
	Long ago, prophets knew	118
1:26-35	Of the Father's heart begotten	141
1:26-38	Since the day the angel came	165
	The angel Gabriel from heaven came	172
	The holly and the ivy	175
	When the angel came to Mary	205
1:31	O come, all ye faithful	138
1:35	Gentle Mary laid her child	57
	Glory be to God on high	59
	Hallelu, hallelu, hallelujah	70
	He is born, our Lord and Saviour	81
	Jesus, baby Jesus	99
	Oh town of Bethlehem	143
	Past three o'clock	153
	Wonderful counsellor	209
1:46-55	Earth lies spellbound	47
1:46-49	My soul doth magnify the Lord	132
1:46-47	Sing, all the earth	166
1:48-49	The angel Gabriel from heaven came	172
1:50	Good news	66
1:51-52	Rumours of angels	158
1:51-53	This Child	187
1:54-55	Let me tell you about a baby	111
1:68	On Christmas night all Christians sing	148
	Sing, all the earth	166
1:76	The holly and the ivy	175
1:77-79	From heaven above	53
1:77	Journey to Bethlehem	105
1:77-79	Joyful, joyful we adore thee	106
1:77	No room for the Saviour	135
1:77-79	On Christmas night all Christians sing	148
1:77-79	People awaken, open your eyes	155
	Ring out the bells	157
1:78	Good news	66
1:78-79	Now dawns the sun of righteousness	136
1:78	O come, O come Emmanuel	140
1:78-79	This Child	187
1:79	O come and join the dance	139
2:4-20	A baby was born in Bethlehem	1
2:4-7	Away in a manger	14
	Born in the night, Mary's child	16
2:4-20	C is for the Christ Child	23
2:4-7	Child in the manger	24
	Child of the stable's secret birth	25
	Christmas bells that bring	27
	Christmas, it's Christmas	30
	Christmas without Jesus	31
2:4-20	Come and join the celebration	32
2:4-7	Come and praise the Lord our King	33
	Come, come, come to the manger	34
2:4-20	Come now with awe	35

Luke

	Come, watch with us	38
	Crackers and turkeys	39
2:4-20	Cradled in a manger	40
2:4-7	Cradle rocking	41
	Down from his glory	45
	Earth gave him no welcome	46
	Earth lies spellbound	47
	Every Christmas	50
2:4-20	From heaven above	53
2:4-7	From the heights of glory	55
	From the squalor of a borrowed stable	56
2:4-20	Gentle Mary laid her child	57
	Girls and boys, leave your toys	58
2:4-14	Glory to God in the highest	60
2:4-20	God rest you merry, gentlemen	62
2:4-14	Good Christians all, rejoice	64
2:4-20	Hallelu, hallelu, hallelujah	70
	Happy day of great rejoicing	73
	Hark to the story	76
2:4-7	Hear the sound of people singing	77
	Hee, haw! Hee, haw!	80
	He is born, our Lord and Saviour	81
2:4-20	Here we go to Bethlehem	82
	Holy child	84
2:4-7	Holy, holy Lord	85
	How far is it to Bethlehem?	86
	Immanuel, God is with us	87
	In a very ordinary stable	89
2:4-14	Infant holy, infant lowly	90
2:4-7	in the bleak midwinter	91
2:4-14	In the firelight	92
2:4-7	Into darkness light has broken	93
2:4-20	It was on a starry night	97
2:4-7	I wonder as I wander	98
2:4-20	Jesus Christ the Lord is born	101
2:4-7	Jesus, my Saviour	103
	Journey to Bethlehem	105
	Let me tell you about a baby	111
	Little donkey	115
	Little Jesus, sweetly sleep	116
2:4-20	Long ago and far away	117
2:4-7	Long ago, prophets knew	118
2:4-14	Long ago there was born	119
2:4-20	Long time ago in Bethlehem	120
	Look away to Bethlehem	121
	Look to the skies	122
2:4-7	Lord, you left your throne	124
	Lully, lulla, thou little tiny child	126
	Mary had a baby	127
	Mary had a little baby	128
2:4-20	Mary, Joseph, manger and straw	129
2:4-7	Mary shivers	130
	No gift so wonderful	133
	No room at the world	134
	No room for the Saviour	135
2:4-20	O come and join the dance	139
	Oh, come, little children	142
	Oh town of Bethlehem	143
	O little town of Bethlehem	145
	Once in royal David's city	146
	Over the world this Christmas morn	149
	O what a gift!	150
	O what a mystery I see	151
	Past three o'clock	153
	Ring out the bells	157
2:4-20	Rumours of angels	158
2:4-7	See, amid the winter's snow	159
2:4-20	See him lying on a bed of straw	160
2:4-7	See, to us a child is born	161
	Silently we watch	163
2:4-20	Silent night	164
2:4-7	Since the day the angel came	165

Ref	Title	Page
2:4-7	Sing and celebrate	167
	Sing lullaby!	168
	Sleep, holy child	169
	So many centuries	170
	Thank you, Jesus	171
	The God we seek	174
	The holly and the ivy	175
2:4-20	The promised time arrives	177
2:4-7	There's a special feeling	179
2:4-14	There's a star	180
2:4-20	There's a star in the East	181
2:4-7	There was no room in Bethlehem	182
	The Virgin Mary had a baby boy	184
	This Child	187
	Thou didst leave thy throne	188
	Two thousand years ago	191
	Unto us a boy is born	192
2:4-14	Unto us a child is born	193
2:4-20	We have some news to bring	194
	Welcome the Christ-child	195
	We were not there	197
2:4-7	We will sing your song	198
2:4-20	What child is this?	200
	When God from earth to heaven came down	203
2:4-7	When he comes	204
2:6-7	Jesus, baby Jesus	99
	Jesus born in Bethlehem	100
	Let there be singing	112
2:8-14	Ain't nothing like it	3
2:8-20	All my heart this night rejoices	5
	A long time ago	6
	Angels from the realms of glory	8
	A special star	11
	Behold, the great Creator makes	15
	Carols sing	22
	Christians, awake!	26
	Go, tell it on the mountain	68
	O come, all ye faithful	138
	See, amid the winter's snow	159
	Shepherds found him	162
	The first nowell	173
	The shepherds found the stable	183
	The wise men offer their gifts to him	186
	Tonight	190
	What was it like for the shepherds	202
	While shepherds watched	206
2:10-14	A great and mighty wonder	2
	Break forth, O beauteous heavenly light	17
	Can you believe it?	20
	Child of the stable's secret birth	25
	Christmas without Jesus	31
	Come, come, come to the manger	34
	Come sing the sweet song of the ages	36
	Ding dong, merrily on high	44
	Earth lies spellbound	47
	From the squalor of a borrowed stable	56
	Glory be to God on high	59
	Good news of great joy	67
	Hear the sound of people singing	77
	Heaven invites you to a party	78
	In the bleak midwinter	91
	It came upon the midnight clear	95
	Like a candle flame	114
	Lord, you left your throne	124
	O come and join the dance	139
	Oh town of Bethlehem	143
	O little town of Bethlehem	145
	On Christmas night all Christians sing	148
	Past three o'clock	153
	People awaken, open your eyes	155
	Ring out the bells	157
	Sing lullaby!	168

Ref	Title	Page
2:10-14	Sleep, holy child	169
	The Virgin Mary had a baby boy	184
	Thou didst leave thy throne	188
	We wish you a merry Christmas	199
2:10	Hark, the herald-angels sing	75
2:13-14	Good Christian people	63
2:14-14	It's the time	96
2:14	Joy to the world	108
	Mary had a little baby	128
	Peace to you	154
2:25	Jesus, hope of every nation	102
2:32	Oh town of Bethlehem	143
2:35	Cradle rocking	41
	In the firelight	92
	Since the day the angel came	165
2:52	Thank you, Jesus	171
3:2-6	The holly and the ivy	175
4:2	Who is he, in yonder stall	208
4:18-19	From the squalor of a borrowed stable	56
	Good King Wenceslas	65
	Hark, the glad sound!	74
	He is born, our Lord and Saviour	81
	Once in royal David's city	146
4:40-41	Jesus born in Bethlehem	100
6:12-16	Jesus born in Bethlehem	100
6:38	Good King Wenceslas	65
	Lord, make me thankful	123
7:34	From the squalor of a borrowed stable	56
8:22-25	Child of the stable's secret birth	25
	Jesus born in Bethlehem	100
10:25-37	Amazing grace!	7
14:15-24	Heaven invites you to a party	78
14:16-20	No room at the world	134
15:3-7	Jesus, my Saviour	103
15:11-24	Amazing grace!	7
19:10	Can you believe it?	20
	Earth gave him no welcome	46
	He came in love to bring hope	79
	Holy child	84
	Jesus, my Saviour	103
	Like a candle flame	114
	There was no room in Bethlehem	182
19:41-42	Rumours of angels	158
22:19-20	O what a gift!	150
22:39	Who is he, in yonder stall	208
22:42	Child of the stable's secret birth	25
	From heaven you came	54
22:47-48	No room at the world	134
	Thou didst leave thy throne	188
23:24	Meekness and majesty	131
23:33	Child of the stable's secret birth	25
	Come and praise the Lord our King	33
	From heaven you came	54
	From the heights of glory	55
	From the squalor of a borrowed stable	56
	Jesus born in Bethlehem	100
	Jesus, my Saviour	103
	Lord, you left your throne	124
	Meekness and majesty	131
	No room at the world	134
	No room for the Saviour	135
	O what a gift!	150
23:33-34	Since the day the angel came	165
23:33	Sing lullaby!	168
	There was no room in Bethlehem	182
	Thou didst leave thy throne	188
	Who is he, in yonder stall	208
23:43	Since the day the angel came	165
23:52-53	No room for the Saviour	135
24:6	Come and praise the Lord our King	33
	From the heights of glory	55
	God came among us	61

Luke

24:6	Jesus born in Bethlehem	100
	O what a gift!	150
	Sing lullaby!	168
	Who is he, in yonder stall	208
24:25-27	Come now with awe	35
24:27	Long ago, prophets knew	118
	Of the Father's heart begotten	141

JOHN

1:1-5	Behold, the great Creator makes	15
1:1	Christmas, it's Christmas	30
	Darkness like a shroud	42
1:1-4	Glory be to God on high	59
	God came among us	61
1:1-5	Happy day of great rejoicing	73
	He is born, our Lord and Saviour	81
	Into darkness light has broken	93
1:1	Jesus, hope of every nation	102
	Jesus, name above all names	104
1:1-18	Light shining in the darkness	113
1:1	Lord, you left your throne	124
	Of the Father's heart begotten	141
1:1-3	Once upon a universe	147
	The promised time arrives	177
1:1-2	Thou didst leave thy throne	188
1:1	What child is this?	200
1:1-4	What kind of greatness	201
1:3	Down from his glory	45
	From heaven above	53
1:4-5	Darkness like a shroud	42
	Good Christian people	63
	Good news	66
1:4	Jesus, hope of every nation	102
1:4-5	Joyful, joyful we adore thee	106
	Like a candle flame	114
	No gift so wonderful	133
	Now dawns the sun of righteousness	136
	O come, all ye faithful	138
	O little one sweet, O little one mild	144
	On Christmas night all Christians sing	148
	People awaken, open your eyes	155
	Sing and celebrate	167
	Sleep, holy child	169
	The light of Christ	176
	This Child	187
	We will sing your song	198
1:10-12	Come, come, come to the manger	34
1:10-11	Earth gave him no welcome	46
	Gentle Mary laid her child	57
1:10-14	God came among us	61
1:10-11	Happy day of great rejoicing	73
1:10-13	No gift so wonderful	133
	No room at the world	134
1:10-11	Rumours of angels	158
1:10-13	There was no room in Bethlehem	182
1:10-11	This Child	187
1:10-13	Thou didst leave thy throne	188
1:12-13	A special star	11
	Christmas isn't Christmas	29
	Cradled in a manger	40
	Hark, the herald-angels sing	75
	Hear the sound of people singing	77
	In the firelight	92
1:12-14	Long ago, prophets knew	118
1:12-13	Look to the skies	122
	Lord, you left your throne	124
	No room for the Saviour	135
	O come and join the dance	139
	O little town of Bethlehem	145
	People awaken, open your eyes	155
	So many centuries	170
	The promised time arrives	177

John

1:14	A great and mighty wonder	2
	Behold, the great Creator makes	15
	Break forth, O beauteous heavenly light	17
	Can you believe it?	20
	Child of the stable's secret birth	25
	Christmas, it's Christmas	30
	Come now with awe	35
	Down from his glory	45
	From heaven above	53
	Glory be to God on high	59
	Good news	66
	Happy day of great rejoicing	73
	Hark, the herald-angels sing	75
	He came in love to bring hope	79
	It's the time	96
	Let earth and heaven combine	110
	Let there be singing	112
	Look to the skies	122
	Lord, you left your throne	124
	Meekness and majesty	131
	O come, all ye faithful	138
	Oh town of Bethlehem	143
	O little one sweet, O little one mild	144
	Once in royal David's city	146
	O what a gift!	150
	O what a mystery I see	151
	Silently we watch	163
	Sing, all the earth	166
	The promised time arrives	177
	The Virgin Mary had a baby boy	184
	Thou who wast rich	189
	What kind of greatness	201
	Wonderful counsellor	209
1:16-17	Amazing grace!	7
	Holy child	84
1:17	The promised time arrives	177
1:18	A great and mighty wonder	2
3:3	The light of Christ	176
3:5	The light of Christ	176
3:13	The Virgin Mary had a baby boy	184
3:14	There was no room in Bethlehem	182
3:16	All my heart this night rejoices	5
	At this time of giving	13
	Christians, awake!	26
	Christmas bells that bring	27
	Christmas is a time to love	28
	Christmas without Jesus	31
	Come now with awe	35
	Come, watch with us	38
	From the heights of glory	55
	Good news	66
	Hallelujah!	71
	Hallelujah, my Father	72
	He came in love to bring hope	79
	He is born, our Lord and Saviour	81
	In a very ordinary stable	89
	Into darkness light has broken	93
	Let earth and heaven combine	110
	Let there be singing	112
	Long time ago in Bethlehem	120
	Love came down at Christmas	125
	No gift so wonderful	133
	Over the world this Christmas morn	149
	People awaken, open your eyes	155
	Sing and celebrate	167
	The God we seek	174
	The light of Christ	176
	There's a special feeling	179
	Thou who wast rich	189
	Two thousand years ago	191
	Unto us a boy is born	192
	Unto us a child is born	193

John

3:16	We will sing your song	198
	What kind of greatness	201
	Wonderful counsellor	209
4:14	Joyful, joyful we adore thee	106
4:23-24	O worship the Lord in the beauty of holiness	152
6:35	Cradle rocking	41
8:12	A long time ago	6
	Born in the night, Mary's child	16
	Can you see what we have made?	21
	Cradle rocking	41
	Darkness like a shroud	42
	Jesus, hope of every nation	102
	People awaken, open your eyes	155
	Sing and celebrate	167
	The light of Christ	176
8:32	Lord, you left your throne	124
	Thou didst leave thy throne	188
8:46	Come and praise the Lord our King	33
8:59	Down from his glory	45
9:1-7	Amazing grace!	7
9:5	A long time ago	6
10:27-28	Come and praise the Lord our King	33
10:28	God came among us	61
11:35	Who is he, in yonder stall	208
12:24	Jesus Christ the Lord is born	101
13:5	Meekness and majesty	131
14:6	A special star	11
	Born in the night, Mary's child	16
	The promised time arrives	177
16:22	God came among us	61
	O little one sweet, O little one mild	144
	Who is he, in yonder stall	208
18:1	Who is he, in yonder stall	208
18:2-9	No room at the world	134
18:11	Child of the stable's secret birth	25
19:2	Child of the stable's secret birth	25
	In the firelight	92
19:18	Child of the stable's secret birth	25
	Come and praise the Lord our King	33
	From heaven you came	54
	From the heights of glory	55
	From the squalor of a borrowed stable	56
	Jesus born in Bethlehem	100
	Jesus, my Saviour	103
	Lord, you left your throne	124
	Meekness and majesty	131
	No room at the world	134
	No room for the Saviour	135
	O what a gift!	150
	Since the day the angel came	165
	Sing lullaby!	168
	There was no room in Bethlehem	182
	Thou didst leave thy throne	188
	Who is he, in yonder stall	208
19:38-42	No room for the Saviour	135
	Thou didst leave thy throne	188
20:16	Come and praise the Lord our King	33
	From the heights of glory	55
	God came among us	61
	Jesus born in Bethlehem	100
	O what a gift!	150
	Sing lullaby!	168
	Who is he, in yonder stall	208
20:27	From heaven you came	54
20:28	Wonderful counsellor	209
20:31	Can you believe it?	20
	Come and praise the Lord our King	33
	Hallelujah!	71

ACTS

1:7	From the squalor of a borrowed stable	56
1:8	Now dawns the sun of righteousness	136

Acts

1:11	Born in the night, Mary's child	16
	Lord, you left your throne	124
1:19-20	Rumours of angels	158
10:43	Can you believe it?	20
16:31	Can you believe it?	20
20:35	Good King Wenceslas	65
	Lord, make me thankful	123

ROMANS

1:16	Jesus born in Bethlehem	100
3:24	Amazing grace!	7
5:1-2	Amazing grace!	7
5:1	Child of the stable's secret birth	25
5:1-5	From the heights of glory	55
5:1-2	God came among us	61
5:2	He came in love to bring hope	79
	He is born, our Lord and Saviour	81
	Journey to Bethlehem	105
5:5	He came in love to bring hope	79
5:8	Come now with awe	35
	Hallelujah, my Father	72
	We will sing your song	198
5:10	Hallelujah, my Father	72
8:15	Let earth and heaven combine	110
8:19	Come, watch with us	38
12:11	Like a candle flame	114
13:8	There's a special feeling	179
14:17	Joy to all the world	107
	Now dawns the sun of righteousness	136
15:12	Jesus, hope of every nation	102

1 CORINTHIANS

1:30	Come and praise the Lord our King	33
13:12-13	Let earth and heaven combine	110

2 CORINTHIANS

1:20	O what a mystery I see	151
4:6	The promised time arrives	177
5:18	Hark, the herald-angels sing	75
	Silently we watch	163
5:21	Child in the manger	24
	Silently we watch	163
8:9	Amazing grace!	7
	See him lying on a bed of straw	160
	Thou who wast rich	189
9:15	At this time of giving	13
	Can you believe it?	20
	From the heights of glory	55
	Lord, make me thankful	123
	No gift so wonderful	133
	O what a gift!	150
	Thank you, Jesus	171
13:4	The God we seek	174
13:14	At this time of giving	13

GALATIANS

3:13	O what a mystery I see	151
4:4	Holy child	84
4:4-6	Let earth and heaven combine	110
4:4-5	The promised time arrives	177

EPHESIANS

1:6-7	Amazing grace!	7
1:18	Amazing grace!	7
	From the heights of glory	55
1:21-23	Meekness and majesty	131
1:23	Emmanuel	48

Ephesians

2:1-9	Cradled in a manger	40
2:4-9	Amazing grace!	7
2:4-5	Come now with awe	35
2:6-8	Let earth and heaven combine	110
2:8-9	O what a mystery I see	151
5:8-14	Can you see what we have made?	21
	Darkness like a shroud	42
	Like a candle flame	114
5:8-10	The light of Christ	176
5:14	Earth lies spellbound	47
	People awaken, open your eyes	155
6:10	Darkness like a shroud	42
6:17	Darkness like a shroud	42

PHILIPPIANS

2:4-11	From heaven you came	54
2:5-11	Break forth, O beauteous heavenly light	17
	Come, come, come to the manger	34
	Down from his glory	45
	From the heights of glory	55
	From the squalor of a borrowed stable	56
	Glory be to God on high	59
	Happy day of great rejoicing	73
	Holy child	84
	Let earth and heaven combine	110
	Lord, you left your throne	124
	Silently we watch	163
	Thank you, Jesus	171
	There was no room in Bethlehem	182
	Thou didst leave thy throne	188
	Thou who wast rich	189
	We will sing your song	198
	What kind of greatness	201
2:6-8	Christmas, it's Christmas	30
2:6-9	Meekness and majesty	131
2:9-11	Into darkness light has broken	93
	Jesus, name above all names	104
	Wonderful counsellor	209

COLOSSIANS

1:15-17	Of the Father's heart begotten	141
1:16	Child of the stable's secret birth	25
1:19	Down from his glory	45
1:26-27	O what a mystery I see	151
1:27	From the heights of glory	55
	He came in love to bring hope	79
2:2-3	O what a mystery I see	151
2:13-15	O what a mystery I see	151
	Whiter than the snow	207
2:15	He is born, our Lord and Saviour	81
3:1	Child of the stable's secret birth	25
3:1-4	O what a mystery I see	151
3:17	The wise may bring their learning	185

1 THESSALONIANS

4:16	Born in the night, Mary's child	16
	Earth gave him no welcome	46
4:16-17	From the heights of glory	55
	From the squalor of a borrowed stable	56
	Glory to God in the highest	60
	Jesus, my Saviour	103
	Look to the skies	122
	Lord, you left your throne	124
	Silently we watch	163
	Thou didst leave thy throne	188
5:18	Lord, make me thankful	123

1 TIMOTHY

| 1:17 | Angel-voices ever singing | 10 |
| | Glory be to God on high | 59 |

HEBREWS

2:10	Immanuel, O Immanuel	88
	Meekness and majesty	131
	O little one sweet, O little one mild	144
	Once in royal David's city	146
2:10-18	Once upon a universe	147
2:11-12	Glory be to God on high	59
2:14	O come, O come Emmanuel	140
2:15	Good Christians all, rejoice	64
	He is born, our Lord and Saviour	81
4:15	Come and praise the Lord our King	33
	From the squalor of a borrowed stable	56
	Holy child	84
	Immanuel, O Immanuel	88
	Meekness and majesty	131
	O little one sweet, O little one mild	144
	Once in royal David's city	146
	Once upon a universe	147
	O what a mystery I see	151
5:8	Immanuel, O Immanuel	88
	Meekness and majesty	131
	O little one sweet, O little one mild	144
	Once in royal David's city	146
	Once upon a universe	147
7:25	From the squalor of a borrowed stable	56
13:8	Jesus, my Saviour	103
13:15	The wise may bring their learning	185

JAMES

| 4:7 | O worship the Lord in the beauty of holiness | 152 |

1 PETER

1:10-12	Come now with awe	35
	Come sing the sweet song of the ages	36
	It came upon the midnight clear	95
	Let me tell you about a baby	111
	Long ago, prophets knew	118
	Of the Father's heart begotten	141
	The holly and the ivy	175
	The promised time arrives	177
3:18	Christmas, it's Christmas	30
5:6-7	O worship the Lord in the beauty of holiness	152
5:7	O come and join the dance	139

1 JOHN

2:2	Can you see what we have made?	21
	Child in the manger	24
	Christmas bells that bring	27
	Come and praise the Lord our King	33
	Come now with awe	35
	From the heights of glory	55
	From the squalor of a borrowed stable	56
	Immanuel, O Immanuel	88
	Jesus, my Saviour	103
	O what a mystery I see	151
	See him lying on a bed of straw	160
	There was no room in Bethlehem	182
	Whiter than the snow	207
2:4-7	O what a mystery I see	151
2:12	No room for the Saviour	135
3:8	O come and join the dance	139
4:7-11	Christmas is a time to love	28
4:7	Come and praise the Lord our King	33
	He came in love to bring hope	79
	In a very ordinary stable	89
4:7-12	Joyful, joyful we adore thee	106
4:7	Light shining in the darkness	113
4:7-12	Love came down at Christmas	125
4:7-21	There's a special feeling	179
4:8	Thou who wast rich	189

1 John

4:9-10	Come now with awe	35
	Come, watch with us	38
	What kind of greatness	201
4:10	Christmas bells that bring	27
	Christmas without Jesus	31
	Immanuel, O Immanuel	88
	In a very ordinary stable	89
	Let earth and heaven combine	110
	Let there be singing	112
	O little one sweet, O little one mild	144
	O what a mystery I see	151
	Sing and celebrate	167
	Unto us a child is born	193
	Whiter than the snow	207
4:11	Long ago there was born	119
4:14	Call his name	19
	Down from his glory	45
	From the squalor of a borrowed stable	56
	Hallelujah, my Father	72
	Sleep, holy child	169
	Unto us a child is born	193
4:16	Long ago there was born	119
	Thou who wast rich	189
5:11	Hallelujah!	71
	Hallelujah, my Father	72
	He is born, our Lord and Saviour	81
	Long time ago in Bethlehem	120

REVELATION

1:5	All my heart this night rejoices	5
3:7	O come, O come Emmanuel	140
3:20	Christmas isn't Christmas	29
	Cradled in a manger	40
	Every Christmas	50
	God came among us	61
	Heaven invites you to a party	78
	Look to the skies	122
	No gift so wonderful	133
	No room at the world	134

Revelation

	No room for the Saviour	135
	O come and join the dance	139
	O little town of Bethlehem	145
	O what a gift!	150
	So many centuries	170
	Thou didst leave thy throne	188
5:6	Wonderful counsellor	209
5:9	Christians, awake!	26
	Silently we watch	163
5:11-12	Angel-voices ever singing	10
5:13	Who is he, in yonder stall	208
	Wonderful counsellor	209
6:16	Child of the stable's secret birth	25
7:10	Who is he, in yonder stall	208
	Wonderful counsellor	209
13:8	See, amid the winter's snow	159
19:6-7	Thou didst leave thy throne	188
19:16	All hail King Jesus!	4
	Earth gave him no welcome	46
	From the heights of glory	55
	Silently we watch	163
	Wonderful counsellor	209
20:11	Who is he, in yonder stall	208
21:2	From the squalor of a borrowed stable	56
21:3	As with gladness men of old	12
	Come and praise the Lord our King	33
	Lord, you left your throne	124
	O what a gift!	150
21:4	When he comes	204
21:6	Of the Father's heart begotten	141
22:1-2	Emmanuel, God with us	49
22:3-5	As with gladness men of old	12
22:4	Once in royal David's city	146
	O what a gift!	150
22:5	All hail King Jesus!	4
	Earth lies spellbound	47
22:13	Of the Father's heart begotten	141
22:16	All hail King Jesus!	4
	Hail to the Lord's anointed	69
	He is born, our Lord and Saviour	81
	Into darkness light has broken	93

Key Word Index

ADORATION AND PRAISE-
GODHEAD

A great and mighty wonder 2
Angel-voices ever singing 10
Behold, the great Creator makes 15
Come and praise the Lord
our King 33
Ding dong, merrily on high 44
Glory be to God on high 59
Hallelu, hallelu, hallelujah 70
Hallelujah! 71
Holy, holy Lord 85
It's the time 96
Joy to all the world 107
Let earth and heaven combine 110
My soul doth magnify the Lord 132
O worship the Lord
in the beauty of holiness 152
See, to us a child is born 161
What was it like for
the shepherds 202
While shepherds watched 206

ADORATION AND PRAISE-
JESUS CHRIST

All hail King Jesus! 4
Angels from the realms of glory 8
Angels we have heard on high 9
As with gladness men of old 12
Away in a manger 14
Brightest and best 18
Carols sing 22
Come and praise the Lord
our King 33
Come now with awe 35
Come sing the sweet song
of the ages 36
Come, watch with us 38
Down from his glory 45
For unto us a child is born 51
For unto us a child is born 52
From heaven you came 54
From the heights of glory 55
From the squalor of a
borrowed stable 56
Gentle Mary laid her child 57
Girls and boys, leave your toys 58
Glory be to God on high 59
Glory to God in the highest 60
Good news of great joy 67
Hallelujah, my Father 72
Happy day of great rejoicing 73
Hark, the herald-angels sing 75
Hark to the story 76
He is born, our Lord and Saviour 81
Here we go to Bethlehem 82
His name, his name 83
Immanuel, God is with us 87
Immanuel, O Immanuel 88
Jesus, baby Jesus 99
Jesus, my Saviour 103
Jesus, name above all names 104
Journey to Bethlehem 105
Joyful, joyful we adore thee 106
Let there be singing 112
Light shining in the darkness 113
Look to the skies 122
Meekness and majesty 131
O come, all ye faithful 138

Of the Father's heart begotten 141
O little one sweet,
O little one mild 144
O what a mystery I see 151
Silently we watch 163
Sing, all the earth 166
Sing and celebrate 167
Sleep, holy child 169
The shepherds found the stable 183
The wise men offer their
gifts to him 186
Thou who wast rich 189
Tonight 190
Unto us a child is born 193
Welcome the Christ-child 195
What child is this? 200
What kind of greatness 201
Who is he, in yonder stall 208
Wonderful counsellor 209
Wonderful counsellor,
the mighty God 210

ADORATION AND PRAISE-
THE FATHER

Hallelujah, my Father 72

ADORATION AND PRAISE-
TRINITY

Angel-voices ever singing 10
From heaven above 53
Jesus, hope of every nation 102

CALL TO WORSHIP

Angels from the realms of glory 8
Angels we have heard on high 9
Angel-voices ever singing 10
Come and join the celebration 32
Come and praise the Lord
our King 33
Come, come, come to the manger 34
Come now with awe 35
Earth lies spellbound 47
Good Christian people 63
Good Christians all, rejoice 64
Good news 66
Hark to the story 76
It's the time 96
Joy to all the world 107
O come, all ye faithful 138
O come and join the dance 139
Oh, come, little children 142
People awaken, open your eyes 155

CELEBRATION

A baby was born in Bethlehem 1
Ain't nothing like it 3
All my heart this night rejoices 5
Behold, the great Creator makes 15
Christmas, it's Christmas 30
Christmas without Jesus 31
Come and join the celebration 32
Deck the hall 43
Ding dong, merrily on high 44
Earth lies spellbound 47
Every Christmas 50
Good news 66
Hallelu, hallelu, hallelujah 70

Hallelujah! 71
Happy day of great rejoicing 73
Heaven invites you to a party 78
It's the time 96
Let there be singing 112
O come, all ye faithful 138
O come and join the dance 139
O what a gift! 150
Ring out the bells 157
Sing, all the earth 166
We have some news to bring 194
We will sing your song 198

CHILDREN AND FAMILY
WORSHIP

A baby was born in Bethlehem 1
Ain't nothing like it 3
A long time ago 6
A special star 11
At this time of giving 13
Away in a manger 14
Born in the night, Mary's child 16
Call his name 19
Can you believe it? 20
Can you see what we have made? 21
Carols sing 22
C is for the Christ Child 23
Child in the manger 24
Christmas bells that bring 27
Christmas is a time to love 28
Christmas isn't Christmas 29
Christmas, it's Christmas 30
Christmas without Jesus 31
Come and join the celebration 32
Come and praise the Lord
our King 33
Come, come, come to the manger 34
Crackers and turkeys 39
Cradle rocking 41
Every Christmas 50
Girls and boys, leave your toys 58
Glory to God in the highest 60
Go, tell it on the mountain 68
Hallelu, hallelu, hallelujah 70
Hallelujah! 71
Hark to the story 76
Heaven invites you to a party 78
Hee, haw! Hee, haw! 80
Here we go to Bethlehem 82
How far is it to Bethlehem? 86
In a very ordinary stable 89
Infant holy, infant lowly 90
It's the time 96
It was on a starry night 97
I wonder as I wander 98
Jesus, baby Jesus 99
Jesus born in Bethlehem 100
Journey to Bethlehem 105
Kings came riding 109
Let me tell you about a baby 111
Let there be singing 112
Like a candle flame 114
Little donkey 115
Little Jesus, sweetly sleep 116
Long ago and far away 117
Long ago there was born 119
Long time ago in Bethlehem 120
Look away to Bethlehem 121
Lord, make me thankful 123
Mary had a baby 127

Mary had a little baby 128
Mary, Joseph, manger and straw 129
Mary shivers 130
No room for the Saviour 135
Oh, come, little children 142
Oh town of Bethlehem 143
Once in royal David's city 146
Over the world this
Christmas morn 149
Riding high and low 156
See him lying on a bed of straw 160
Shepherds found him 162
Sing and celebrate 167
Thank you, Jesus 171
There's a special feeling 179
There's a star 180
There's a star in the East 181
The shepherds found the stable 183
The Virgin Mary had a baby boy 184
The wise may bring
their learning 185
The wise men offer their
gifts to him 186
This Child 187
Two thousand years ago 191
Unto us a child is born 193
We have some news to bring 194
Welcome the Christ-child 195
We were not there 197
What was it like for
the shepherds 202

CHRISTINGLE

Can you see what we have made? 21

CHRISTMAS

A baby was born in Bethlehem 1
A great and mighty wonder 2
Ain't nothing like it 3
All my heart this night rejoices 5
A long time ago 6
Angels from the realms of glory 8
Angels we have heard on high 9
A special star 11
As with gladness men of old 12
At this time of giving 13
Away in a manger 14
Born in the night, Mary's child 16
Break forth,
O beauteous heavenly light 17
Brightest and best 18
Call his name 19
Can you believe it? 20
Carols sing 22
C is for the Christ Child 23
Child in the manger 24
Child of the stable's secret birth 25
Christians, awake! 26
Christmas bells that bring 27
Christmas is a time to love 28
Christmas isn't Christmas 29
Christmas, it's Christmas 30
Christmas without Jesus 31
Come and join the celebration 32
Come, come, come to the manger 34
Come now with awe 35
Come sing the sweet song
of the ages 36
Come, watch with us 38

Crackers and turkeys 39
Cradled in a manger 40
Cradle rocking 41
Ding dong, merrily on high 44
Down from his glory 45
Earth gave him no welcome 46
Earth lies spellbound 47
Emmanuel 48
Every Christmas 50
For unto us a child is born 51
For unto us a child is born 52
From heaven above 53
From heaven you came 54
From the heights of glory 55
From the squalor of a
   borrowed stable 56
Gentle Mary laid her child 57
Girls and boys, leave your toys 58
Glory be to God on high 59
Glory to God in the highest 60
God rest you merry, gentlemen 62
Good Christian people 63
Good Christians all, rejoice 64
Good news of great joy 67
Go, tell it on the mountain 68
Hallelu, hallelu, hallelujah 70
Hallelujah! 71
Happy day of great rejoicing 73
Hark, the herald-angels sing 75
Hark to the story 76
Hear the sound of people singing 77
Heaven invites you to a party 78
He came in love to bring hope 79
Hee, haw! Hee, haw! 80
He is born, our Lord and Saviour 81
Here we go to Bethlehem 82
His name, his name 83
Holy child 84
Holy, holy Lord 85
How far is it to Bethlehem? 86
Immanuel, O Immanuel 88
In a very ordinary stable 89
Infant holy, infant lowly 90
In the bleak midwinter 91
In the firelight 92
Into darkness light has broken 93
I saw three ships 94
It came upon the midnight clear 95
It's the time 96
It was on a starry night 97
I wonder as I wander 98
Jesus, baby Jesus 99
Jesus born in Bethlehem 100
Jesus Christ the Lord is born 101
Jesus, hope of every nation 102
Jesus, my Saviour 103
Journey to Bethlehem 105
Kings came riding 109
Let earth and heaven combine 110
Let me tell you about a baby 111
Let there be singing 112
Like a candle flame 114
Little donkey 115
Little Jesus, sweetly sleep 116
Long ago and far away 117
Long ago, prophets knew 118
Long ago there was born 119
Long time ago in Bethlehem 120
Look away to Bethlehem 121
Look to the skies 122
Lord, make me thankful 123
Lord, you left your throne 124
Love came down at Christmas 125
Lully, lulla, thou little tiny child 126

Mary had a baby 127
Mary had a little baby 128
Mary, Joseph, manger and straw 129
Mary shivers 130
No gift so wonderful 133
No room at the world 134
No room for the Saviour 135
Now dawns the sun of
   righteousness 136
O Christmas tree 137
O come, all ye faithful 138
O come and join the dance 139
O come, O come Emmanuel 140
Of the Father's heart begotten 141
Oh, come, little children 142
Oh town of Bethlehem 143
O little one sweet,
   O little one mild 144
O little town of Bethlehem 145
Once in royal David's city 146
Once upon a universe 147
On Christmas night
   all Christians sing 148
Over the world this
   Christmas morn 149
O what a gift! 150
O what a mystery I see 151
Past three o'clock 153
People awaken, open your eyes 155
Riding high and low 156
Ring out the bells 157
Rumours of angels 158
See, amid the winter's snow 159
See him lying on a bed of straw 160
See, to us a child is born 161
Shepherds found him 162
Silently we watch 163
Silent night 164
Since the day the angel came 165
Sing, all the earth 166
Sing and celebrate 167
Sing lullaby! 168
Sleep, holy child 169
So many centuries 170
Thank you, Jesus 171
The angel Gabriel from
   heaven came 172
The first nowell 173
The God we seek 174
The holly and the ivy 175
The light of Christ 176
The promised time arrives 177
The race that long in
   darkness pined 178
There's a special feeling 179
There's a star 180
There's a star in the East 181
There was no room in Bethlehem 182
The shepherds found the stable 183
The Virgin Mary had a baby boy 184
The wise may bring
   their learning 185
The wise men offer their
   gifts to him 186
This Child 187
Thou didst leave thy throne 188
Thou who wast rich 189
Tonight 190
Two thousand years ago 191
Unto us a boy is born 192
Unto us a child is born 193
We have some news to bring 194
Welcome the Christ-child 195
We three kings of Orient are 196

We were not there 197
We will sing your song 198
We wish you a merry Christmas 199
What child is this? 200
What kind of greatness 201
What was it like for
   the shepherds 202
When God from earth
   to heaven came down 203
When he comes 204
When the angel came to Mary 205
While shepherds watched 206
Who is he, in yonder stall 208

**CHURCH-FELLOWSHIP
AND UNITY**

At this time of giving 13

CHURCH-NATURE

Emmanuel 48
Emmanuel, God with us 49

CLOSING OF SERVICE

Peace to you 154

**COMMITMENT AND
CONSECRATION**

Darkness like a shroud 42
Down from his glory 45
From heaven you came 54
Look to the skies 122
Lord, you left your throne 124
No room for the Saviour 135
O little town of Bethlehem 145
O what a mystery I see 151
People awaken, open your eyes 155
The wise may bring
   their learning 185
Thou didst leave thy throne 188
We will sing your song 198
What kind of greatness 201

DELIVERANCE

Break forth,
   O beauteous heavenly light 17

DESIRE FOR GOD

As with gladness men of old 12
Away in a manger 14
Cradled in a manger 40
Lord, you left your throne 124

EASTER

Child of the stable's secret birth 25
Hallelujah, my Father 72
Meekness and majesty 131
Whiter than the snow 207

FAITH AND HOPE

Break forth,
   O beauteous heavenly light 17
Can you believe it? 20
Emmanuel, God with us 49
From the heights of glory 55
He came in love to bring hope 79
Jesus, hope of every nation 102

GOD-CREATION

Can you see what we have made? 21

GOD-GRACE

Amazing grace! 7
At this time of giving 13
Christmas bells that bring 27
Meekness and majesty 131
O what a gift! 150
O worship the Lord
   in the beauty of holiness 152

GOD-HOLINESS

O worship the Lord
   in the beauty of holiness 152

GOD-MAJESTY AND POWER

Meekness and majesty 131

GOD-MERCY

Come, come, come to the manger 34
Good news 66
Hail to the Lord's anointed 69
In a very ordinary stable 89

**GOD-PROTECTION,
CARE AND GUIDANCE**

Away in a manger 14

GOD-PROVISION

At this time of giving 13

HEALING

Hark, the glad sound! 74

HEAVEN

Angel-voices ever singing 10
As with gladness men of old 12

HOLINESS AND PURITY

Darkness like a shroud 42

JESUS-ADVENT AND BIRTH

A baby was born in Bethlehem 1
A great and mighty wonder 2
Ain't nothing like it 3
All my heart this night rejoices 5
A long time ago 6
Angels from the realms of glory 8
Angels we have heard on high 9
A special star 11
As with gladness men of old 12
Away in a manger 14
Behold, the great Creator makes 15
Born in the night, Mary's child 16
Break forth,
   O beauteous heavenly light 17
Call his name 19
Can you believe it? 20
Carols sing 22
C is for the Christ Child 23
Child in the manger 24
Child of the stable's secret birth 25
Christians, awake! 26

Christmas, it's Christmas 30
Christmas without Jesus 31
Come and join the celebration 32
Come, come, come to the manger 34
Come now with awe 35
Come, thou long-expected Jesus 37
Come, watch with us 38
Crackers and turkeys 39
Cradled in a manger 40
Cradle rocking 41
Darkness like a shroud 42
Down from his glory 45
Earth gave him no welcome 46
Earth lies spellbound 47
Emmanuel 48
For unto us a child is born 51
For unto us a child is born 52
From heaven above 53
From heaven you came 54
From the heights of glory 55
From the squalor of a
    borrowed stable 56
Gentle Mary laid her child 57
Girls and boys, leave your toys 58
Glory be to God on high 59
Glory to God in the highest 60
God came among us 61
God rest you merry, gentlemen 62
Good Christian people 63
Good Christians all, rejoice 64
Good news 66
Good news of great joy 67
Go, tell it on the mountain 68
Hallelu, hallelu, hallelujah 70
Hallelujah! 71
Happy day of great rejoicing 73
Hark, the glad sound! 74
Hark, the herald-angels sing 75
Hark to the story 76
Heaven invites you to a party 78
He came in love to bring hope 79
Hee, haw! Hee, haw! 80
He is born, our Lord and Saviour 81
Here we go to Bethlehem 82
Holy child 84
Holy, holy Lord 85
How far is it to Bethlehem? 86
Immanuel, God is with us 87
Immanuel, O Immanuel 88
Infant holy, infant lowly 90
In the bleak midwinter 91
In the firelight 92
Into darkness light has broken 93
It came upon the midnight clear 95
It's the time 96
It was on a starry night 97
I wonder as I wander 98
Jesus, baby Jesus 99
Jesus born in Bethlehem 100
Jesus Christ the Lord is born 101
Jesus, hope of every nation 102
Jesus, my Saviour 103
Journey to Bethlehem 105
Joy to the world 108
Kings came riding 109
Let earth and heaven combine 110
Let me tell you about a baby 111
Let there be singing 112
Like a candle flame 114
Little donkey 115
Little Jesus, sweetly sleep 116
Long ago and far away 117
Long ago, prophets knew 118
Long ago there was born 119

Long time ago in Bethlehem 120
Look away to Bethlehem 121
Look to the skies 122
Lord, you left your throne 124
Love came down at Christmas 125
Lully, lulla, thou little tiny child 126
Mary had a baby 127
Mary had a little baby 128
Mary, Joseph, manger and straw 129
Mary shivers 130
My soul doth magnify the Lord 132
No gift so wonderful 133
No room at the world 134
No room for the Saviour 135
Now dawns the sun
    of righteousness 136
O come, all ye faithful 138
O come and join the dance 139
O come, O come Emmanuel 140
Of the Father's heart begotten 141
Oh, come, little children 142
Oh town of Bethlehem 143
O little one sweet,
    O little one mild 144
O little town of Bethlehem 145
Once in royal David's city 146
Once upon a universe 147
On Christmas night
    all Christians sing 148
Over the world this
    Christmas morn 149
O what a gift! 150
O what a mystery I see 151
Past three o'clock 153
People awaken, open your eyes 155
Riding high and low 156
Ring out the bells 157
Rumours of angels 158
See, amid the winter's snow 159
See him lying on a bed of straw 160
See, to us a child is born 161
Shepherds found him 162
Silently we watch 163
Silent night 164
Since the day the angel came 165
Sing, all the earth 166
Sing and celebrate 167
Sing lullaby! 168
Sleep, holy child 169
So many centuries 170
Thank you, Jesus 171
The angel Gabriel from
    heaven came 172
The first nowell 173
The God we seek 174
The holly and the ivy 175
The light of Christ 176
The promised time arrives 177
The race that long in
    darkness pined 178
There's a special feeling 179
There's a star 180
There's a star in the East 181
There was no room
    in Bethlehem 182
The shepherds found the stable 183
The Virgin Mary had a baby boy 184
The wise may bring
    their learning 185
The wise men offer
    their gifts to him 186
This Child 187
Thou didst leave thy throne 188
Thou who wast rich 189

Tonight 190
Two thousand years ago 191
Unto us a boy is born 192
Unto us a child is born 193
We have some news to bring 194
Welcome the Christ-child 195
We three kings of Orient are 196
We were not there 197
We will sing your song 198
What child is this? 200
What kind of greatness 201
What was it like for
    the shepherds 202
When God from earth
    to heaven came down 203
When he comes 204
When the angel came to Mary 205
While shepherds watched 206
Who is he, in yonder stall 208

JESUS-ATONEMENT,
SUFFERING AND DEATH

Child of the stable's secret birth 25
Down from his glory 45
Earth gave him no welcome 46
From heaven you came 54
From the heights of glory 55
From the squalor of a
    borrowed stable 56
God came among us 61
Hallelujah, my Father 72
Holy child 84
Immanuel, God is with us 87
Immanuel, O Immanuel 88
In the firelight 92
Jesus born in Bethlehem 100
Jesus, my Saviour 103
Lord, you left your throne 124
Meekness and majesty 131
No room at the world 134
No room for the Saviour 135
O what a gift! 150
O what a mystery I see 151
Since the day the angel came 165
Sing lullaby! 168
There was no room
    in Bethlehem 182
Thou didst leave thy throne 188
Whiter than the snow 207
Who is he, in yonder stall 208

JESUS-INCARNATION

A baby was born in Bethlehem 1
A great and mighty wonder 2
All my heart this night rejoices 5
A long time ago 6
Angels from the realms of glory 8
Angels we have heard on high 9
A special star 11
Away in a manger 14
Behold, the great Creator makes
Break forth,
    O beauteous heavenly light 17
Call his name 19
Can you believe it? 20
Child of the stable's secret birth 25
Christmas, it's Christmas 30
Come now with awe 35
Down from his glory 45
Earth gave him no welcome 46
Emmanuel 48
Emmanuel, God with us 49

For unto us a child is born 51
For unto us a child is born 52
From heaven above 53
From the heights of glory 55
From the squalor of a
    borrowed stable 56
Glory be to God on high 59
God came among us 61
Good news 66
Hail to the Lord's anointed 69
Hallelujah, my Father 72
Happy day of great rejoicing 73
Hark, the herald-angels sing 75
He came in love to bring hope 79
He is born, our Lord and Saviour 81
His name, his name 83
Holy child 84
How far is it to Bethlehem? 86
Immanuel, God is with us 87
Immanuel, O Immanuel 88
In a very ordinary stable 89
In the bleak midwinter 91
Into darkness light has broken 93
Let earth and heaven combine 110
Let there be singing 112
Light shining in the darkness 113
Look to the skies 122
Meekness and majesty 131
Now dawns the sun
    of righteousness 136
O come, all ye faithful 138
Of the Father's heart begotten 141
O little one sweet,
    O little one mild 144
O little town of Bethlehem 145
Once upon a universe 147
Over the world this
    Christmas morn 149
O what a gift! 150
O what a mystery I see 151
Rumours of angels 158
See, amid the winter's snow 159
Silently we watch 163
Silent night 164
Since the day the angel came 165
Sing, all the earth 166
Sing and celebrate 167
The light of Christ 176
The promised time arrives 177
There's a star 180
There was no room
    in Bethlehem 182
The Virgin Mary had a baby boy 184
Thou didst leave thy throne 188
Thou who wast rich 189
Tonight 190
Two thousand years ago 191
Unto us a boy is born 192
We will sing your song 198
What child is this? 200
What kind of greatness 201
When God from earth
    to heaven came down 203
When he comes 204
While shepherds watched 206
Wonderful counsellor 209
Wonderful counsellor,
    the mighty God 210

JESUS-KINGSHIP
AND KINGDOM

All hail King Jesus! 4
Born in the night, Mary's child 16

Break forth,
   O beauteous heavenly light 17
Can you see what we have made? 21
Carols sing 22
Child of the stable's secret birth 25
Christians, awake! 26
Come, thou long-expected Jesus 37
Cradle rocking 41
Darkness like a shroud 42
Earth gave him no welcome 46
Earth lies spellbound 47
For unto us a child is born 51
For unto us a child is born 52
From heaven you came 54
From the heights of glory 55
From the squalor of a
   borrowed stable 56
Good King Wenceslas 65
Hail to the Lord's anointed 69
Hark, the glad sound! 74
He came in love to bring hope 79
He is born, our Lord and Saviour 81
His name, his name 83
In the firelight 92
Into darkness light has broken 93
It came upon the midnight clear 95
Jesus born in Bethlehem 100
Joy to the world 108
Look to the skies 122
Lord, you left your throne 124
Meekness and majesty 131
Now dawns the sun
   of righteousness 136
O come and join the dance 139
O come, O come Emmanuel 140
Once in royal David's city 146
O what a mystery I see 151
Silently we watch 163
The holly and the ivy 175
The promised time arrives 177
The race that long in
   darkness pined 178
Thou didst leave thy throne 188
We will sing your song 198
What kind of greatness 201
When he comes 204
Who is he, in yonder stall 208

JESUS–LIFE

From the heights of glory 55
From the squalor of a
   borrowed stable 56
Holy child 84
Immanuel, O Immanuel 88
Jesus born in Bethlehem 100
Jesus, my Saviour 103
Lord, you left your throne 124
Once in royal David's city 146
Once upon a universe 147
Since the day the angel came 165
Who is he, in yonder stall 208

JESUS–LORDSHIP

Child of the stable's secret birth 25
Christmas, it's Christmas 30
Christmas without Jesus 31
Holy child 84
Into darkness light has broken 93
Jesus, name above all names 104
Who is he, in yonder stall 208
Wonderful counsellor 209
Wonderful counsellor,
   the mighty God 210

JESUS–NAME AND GLORY

All hail King Jesus! 4
Brightest and best 18
Immanuel, O Immanuel 88
Jesus, name above all names 104
Wonderful counsellor 209
Wonderful counsellor,
   the mighty God 210

JESUS–RESURRECTION

Joy to all the world 107
O what a gift! 150
Sing lullaby! 168
Who is he, in yonder stall 208

JESUS–SAVIOUR

Child in the manger 24
Sleep, holy child 169

JESUS–SECOND COMING

Earth gave him no welcome 46
From the squalor of a
   borrowed stable 56
Jesus, my Saviour 103
Joy to the world 108
O what a gift! 150
Silently we watch 163
Thou didst leave thy throne 188
When he comes 204

JOY

Ain't nothing like it 3
All my heart this night rejoices 5
Deck the hall 43
God rest you merry, gentlemen 62
Good Christian people 63
Good Christians all, rejoice 64
Good news 66
Good news of great joy 67
Hallelu, hallelu, hallelujah 70
Hallelujah! 71
Happy day of great rejoicing 73
Heaven invites you to a party 78
It's the time 96
Joyful, joyful we adore thee 106
Joy to all the world 107
Joy to the world 108
Let there be singing 112
Light shining in the darkness 113
O come and join the dance 139
O what a gift! 150
Ring out the bells 157
Sing, all the earth 166
We will sing your song 198

JUSTICE

Amazing grace! 7
Darkness like a shroud 42
Earth lies spellbound 47
Good King Wenceslas 65
Hail to the Lord's anointed 69
Hark, the glad sound! 74
Hear the sound of people singing 77
Rumours of angels 158
We will sing your song 198
When he comes 204

LOVE–GOD'S LOVE

Christmas is a time to love 28
Come now with awe 35
From the heights of glory 55
Hallelujah! 71
In a very ordinary stable 89
Joyful, joyful we adore thee 106
Joy to the world 108
Let earth and heaven combine 110
Let there be singing 112
Long ago there was born 119
Love came down at Christmas 125
Oh town of Bethlehem 143
Over the world this
   Christmas morn 149
The God we seek 174
There's a special feeling 179
Thou who wast rich 189
Two thousand years ago 191
Unto us a child is born 193
We will sing your song 198
What kind of greatness 201

LOVE–OUR LOVE FOR OTHERS

Amazing grace! 7
Christmas is a time to love 28
Lord, make me thankful 123
Love came down at Christmas 125
There's a special feeling 179
We will sing your song 198

MISSION

Can you believe it? 20
Christmas isn't Christmas 29
Earth lies spellbound 47
From heaven above 53
From heaven you came 54
God came among us 61
Hear the sound of people singing 77
Heaven invites you to a party 78
He came in love to bring hope 79
In the firelight 92
Like a candle flame 114
No gift so wonderful 133
No room at the world 134
No room for the Saviour 135
Now dawns the sun
   of righteousness 136
O come and join the dance 139
Rumours of angels 158
So many centuries 170
There was no room in
   Bethlehem 182
We will sing your song 198

NEW YEAR

Deck the hall 43

OFFERING

At this time of giving 13
Brightest and best 18
From heaven you came 54
In the bleak midwinter 91
There's a special feeling 179
The wise may bring their
   learning 185
We three kings of Orient are 196
What kind of greatness 201

PEACE

Peace to you 154

PROCLAMATION

All hail King Jesus! 4
Behold, the great Creator makes 15
Break forth,
   O beauteous heavenly light 17
Earth lies spellbound 47
Emmanuel, God with us 49
From the heights of glory 55
Good Christians all, rejoice 64
Go, tell it on the mountain 68
Hark, the herald-angels sing 75
Immanuel, God is with us 87
Into darkness light has broken 93
Joy to all the world 107
Light shining in the darkness 113
Now dawns the sun
   of righteousness 136

RENEWAL

Emmanuel, God with us 49

REPENTANCE AND
FORGIVENESS

Come, come, come to the manger 34
Journey to Bethlehem 105
Whiter than the snow 207

ROUNDS/ANTIPHONAL
SONGS

A baby was born in Bethlehem 1
A long time ago 6
Good news of great joy 67
He came in love to bring hope 79
Like a candle flame 114
Mary, Joseph, manger and straw 129
O come and join the dance 139
Sing, all the earth 166
Sing and celebrate 167
The light of Christ 176
Tonight 190

SALVATION AND REDEMPTION

All my heart this night rejoices 5
A long time ago 6
Amazing grace! 7
A special star 11
Call his name 19
Child in the manger 24
Christmas isn't Christmas 29
Come and praise the
   Lord our King 33
Come now with awe 35
Come, thou long-expected Jesus 37
Cradled in a manger 40
Down from his glory 45
Earth gave him no welcome 46
From the squalor of a
   borrowed stable 56
God came among us 61
Good news 66
Good news of great joy 67
Hallelujah, my Father 72
Hark, the herald-angels sing 75
He came in love to bring hope 79
He is born, our Lord and Saviour 81

Immanuel, God is with us 87
In a very ordinary stable 89
Into darkness light has broken 93
Jesus, my Saviour 103
Journey to Bethlehem 105
Let earth and heaven combine 110
Meekness and majesty 131
Now dawns the sun
  of righteousness 136
O come, O come Emmanuel 140
On Christmas night
  all Christians sing 148

O what a mystery I see 151
People awaken, open your eyes 155
Rumours of angels 158
Silently we watch 163
The God we seek 174
There was no room
  in Bethlehem 182

SOCIAL CONCERN

Amazing grace! 7
Darkness like a shroud 42

Earth lies spellbound 47
Good King Wenceslas 65
Hail to the Lord's anointed 69
Hark, the glad sound! 74
Hear the sound of people singing 77
Rumours of angels 158
We will sing your song 198
When he comes 204

SUBMISSION TO GOD

O worship the Lord
  in the beauty of holiness 152

THANKSGIVING

Angel-voices ever singing 10
Christmas, it's Christmas 30
Lord, make me thankful 123
Thank you, Jesus 171
There's a special feeling 179
Whiter than the snow 207

Index of First Lines and Titles

This index gives the first line of each hymn. If a hymn is known by an alternative title, this is also given, but indented and in italics.

A

A baby was born in Bethlehem	1
A great and mighty wonder	2
Ain't nothing like it	3
All hail King Jesus!	4
All my heart this night rejoices	5
A long time ago	6
Amazing grace!	7
Amazing grace - I was homeless	7
Angels from the realms of glory	8
Angels we have heard on high	9
Angel-voices ever singing	10
Anno Domini	107
Arise, shine!	42
A special star	11
A starry night	97
As with gladness men of old	12
At this time of giving	13
Away in a manger	14

B

Beautiful night	92
Behold, the great Creator makes	15
Born in the night, Mary's child	16
Break forth, O beauteous heavenly light	17
Brightest and best	18

C

Call his name	19
Can you believe it	20
Can you see what we have made	21
Carols sing	22
C for the Christ Child	23
Child in the manger	24
Child of the stable's secret birth	25
Christians, awake!	26
Christmas bells that bring	27
Christmas calypso	111
Christmas is a time to love	28
Christmas isn't Christmas	29
Christmas, it's Christmas	30
Christmas without Jesus	31
Come and join the celebration	32
Come and praise the Lord our King	33
Come, come, come to the manger	34
Come now with awe	35
Come sing the sweet song of the ages	36
Come, thou long-expected Jesus	37
Come, watch with us	38
Coventry Carol	126
Crackers and turkeys	39
Cradled in a manger	40
Cradle rocking	41

D

Darkness like a shroud	42
Deck the hall	43
Ding dong, merrily on high!	44
Down from his glory	45

E

Earth gave him no welcome	46
Earth lies spellbound	47
Emmanuel	48
Emmanuel, God is with us	49
Every Christmas	50

F

For unto us a child is born	51
For unto us a child is born	52
From heaven above	53
From heaven you came	54
From the heights of glory	55
From the squalor of a borrowed stable	56

G

Gentle Mary laid her child	57
Girls and boys, leave your toys	58
Glory be to God on high	59
Glory to God	190
Glory to God in the highest	60
God came among us	61
God rest you merry, gentlemen	62
Good Christian people	63
Good Christians all, rejoice	64
Good King Wenceslas	65
Good news	66
Good news of great joy	67
Go, tell it on the mountain	68

H

Hail to the Lord's anointed	69
Hallelu, hallelu, hallelujah	70
Hallelujah!	71
Hallelujah, my Father	72
Happy day of great rejoicing	73
Hark, the glad sound!	74
Hark, the herald-angels sing	75
Hark to the story	76
Have we any room for Jesus?	133
Hear the sound of people singing	77
Heaven invites you to a party	78
Heaven's gift of love	27
He came in love to bring hope	79
Hee, haw! Hee, haw!	80
He is born, our Lord and Saviour	81
Here we come to Bethlehem	82
His name, his name	83
Holy child	84
Holy, holy Lord	85
How far is it to Bethlehem?	86

I

Immanuel	56
Immanuel, God is with us	87
Immanuel, O Immanuel	88
In a very ordinary stable	89
Infant holy, infant lowly	90
In the bleak midwinter	91
In the firelight	92
In the stable	183
Into darkness light has broken	93
I saw three ships	94
It came upon the midnight clear	95
It's Christmas time again	179
It's the time	96
It was on a starry night	97
I wonder as I wander	98

J

Jesus, baby Jesus	99
Jesus born in Bethlehem	100
Jesus Christ the Lord is born	101
Jesus, hope of every nation	102
Jesus is born	129
Jesus, my Saviour	103
Jesus, name above all names	104

J (continued)

Journey to Bethlehem	105
Joyful, joyful, we adore thee	106
Joy to all the world	107
Joy to the world	108

K

Kings came riding	109

L

Let earth and heaven combine	110
Let me tell you about a baby	111
Let there be singing	112
Light of the world	155
Light shining in the darkness	113
Like a candle flame	114
Little donkey	115
Little Jesus, sweetly sleep	116
Long ago and far away	117
Long ago, prophets knew	118
Long ago there was born	119
Long time ago in Bethlehem	120
Look away to Bethlehem	121
Look no further	89
Look to the skies	122
Lord, make me thankful	123
Lord, you left your throne	124
Love came down at Christmas	125
Lully, lulla, thou little tiny child	126

M

Mary had a baby	127
Mary had a little baby	128
Mary, Joseph, manger and straw	129
Mary's boy child	120
Mary's child	130
Mary shivers	130
Mary woke with a start one night	19
Meekness and majesty	131
My soul doth magnify the Lord	132

N

No gift so wonderful	133
No room at the world	134
No room for the Saviour	135
Nothing will ever be the same	170
Now dawns the sun of righteousness	136

O

O Christmas tree	137
O come, all ye faithful	138
O come and join the dance	139
O come, O come Emmanuel	140
Of the Father's heart begotten	141
Oh, come, little children	142
Oh town of Bethlehem	143
O little one sweet, O little one mild	144
O little town of Bethlehem	145
Once in royal David's city	146
Once upon a universe	147
On Christmas night all Christians sing	148
Over the world this Christmas morn	149
O what a gift!	150
O what a mystery I see	151
O worship the Lord in the beauty of holiness	152

P

Past three o'clock	153
Peace to you	154
People awaken, open your eyes	155

R

Riding high	156
Riding high and low	156
Ring out the bells	157
Rise up, shepherd, and follow	181
Rumours of angels	158

S

See, amid the winter's snow	159
See him lying on a bed of straw	160
Seeking for me!	103
See, to us a child is born	161
Shepherds found him	162
Silently we watch	163
Silent night	164
Since the day the angel came	165
Sing, all the earth	166
Sing and celebrate	167
Sing a song about Christmas	23
Sing Hosannas	76
Sing lullaby!	168
Sleep, holy child	169
So many centuries	170
Somebody's birthday	39
Song for Christingle	21
Song of Immanuel	36

T

Tell out, tell out the news	136
Thank you, Jesus	171
The angel Gabriel from heaven came	172

The candle song	114
The Christmas Child	77
The donkey's Christmas carol	80
The first Nowell	173
The giving song	13
The God we seek	174
The holly and the ivy	175
The Holy Gospel	100
The light of Christ	176
The promised time arrives	177
The race that long in darkness pined	178
There's a special feeling	179
There's a star	180
There's a star in the East	181
There was no room in Bethlehem	182
The Servant King	54
The shepherds found the stable	183
The Virgin Mary had a baby boy	184
The wise may bring their learning	185
The wise men offer their gifts to him	186
This Child	187
This is your God	131
Thorns in the straw	165
Thou didst leave thy throne	188
Thou who wast rich	189
Tonight	190
Two thousand years ago	191

U

Unto us a boy is born	192
Unto us a child is born	193

W

We have found him	162
We have some news to bring	194
Welcome the Christ-child	195
We three kings of Orient are	196
We were not there	197
We will sing your song	198
We wish you a merry Christmas	199
What a gift	55
What child is this	200
What kind of greatness	201
What was it like for the shepherds	202
When God from heaven to earth came down	203
When he comes	204
When the angel came to Mary	205
While shepherds watched	206
Whiter than the snow	207
Who is he, in yonder stall	208
Wonderful counsellor	209
Wonderful counsellor, the mighty God	210
Worship song	186
Worship the King	122

Y

You came from the highest	198

Also available from Kevin Mayhew

Christmas Carol Sheet

A tremendously useful carol sheet, containing the
most popular carols and Christmas songs, for use in every
kind of situation that involves carol singing.

Angels from the realms of glory
As with gladness
Away in a manger
Christians, awake
Ding dong, merrily on high!
Good Christians, all, rejoice
Good King Wenceslas
Hark, the herald-angels sing
In the bleak mid-winter
Infant holy, infant lowly
Love came down at Christmas
O come, all ye faithful
O little town of Bethlehem
On Christmas night all Christians sing
Once in royal David's city
See amid the winter's snow
See him lying on a bed of straw
Silent night
The first Nowell
The holly and the ivy
This child
Unto us a boy is born
We three kings
While shepherds watched

1470134
1 84003 956 6